THE NAUGHTY COUPLE'S BUCKET LIST

101 Ways to Spice Up Your Love Life
and Strengthen Your Relationship

Nicole Jones

ISBN: 979-8-88768-011-8

CONTENTS

INTRODUCTION

So, you want to spice up your love life, do you? Did the title *Naughty Couple's* get you exited? Are you hoping to have found the answers, the holy grail to becoming a sexual expert?

In opening up this book, you have committed to both you and your partnership, to dive a little deeper into the juicy, infinite world of sexuality. The phrase "spicing things up in the bedroom" can mean something different to everyone, so it will be important to embark on this journey with the understanding that your sexual experience will most likely be different from everyone else's, including your partner. Therefore, you must integrate the concepts and practices in this book at a pace that feels applicable and approachable to you. I will not suggest you take things at a pace that feels comfortable, because this book is offered to encourage you to push yourself out of your comfort zone. After all, that's why you've started this journey, is it not?

Rather, I say applicable and approachable, because it will not do your sex life any good to dive in headfirst and end up caught in a state of being overwhelmed that causes you to put the book down and walk away from sexual exploration completely. This may sound dramatic, but sexuality is extremely vulnerable, and whether we like to admit it or not, exploring our sexuality is one of the scariest things we can do.

Sexuality is scary simply because we have never been properly taught how to do it. There is no rule book, no "right way," no laws or regulations or governing bodies. There is rarely even any conversation on the matter! It's continuously evolving and changing, and just when we think we've got it, something will snatch our confidence away in a flash.

By the same token, however, sexuality is scary precisely because of the many different rule books by which it is governed. Each of us, based on the family and house in which we were raised, the culture we belong to, the society we are a part of, our geographical location, our gender, our previous sexual experiences, and many more factors, will develop our own perceptions of sex, and this very much regulates our sexual interactions.

Ultimately, sexuality is scary because it is extremely vulnerable, and we've also not been taught how to be vulnerable. Sexuality is a laying of the self out to be received by another, it is a window into our minds, our bodies, our emotions, our fears, and our deepest desires, and in a world that values intellect, reason, and discipline, vulnerability is rarely safe.

The operating premise of this book, then, is that good old-fashioned communication is the very first step and the main ingredient in "spicing up your sex life." There is no way around it. There is no shortcut. If you are not willing to communicate, you will get nowhere with these chapters. Sure, you may have an orgasm or two, but without communication, you may as well stay loyal to your tried-and-true routine, the very one that brought you here and caused you to desire to spice things up. Even masturbation requires communication!

Once we have waded through the murky waters of communication, once we have graduated kindergarten, then we can start to have a little more fun and get a little naughtier, as promised. You're invited to use this book as a tool in your toolbox on your sexual journey. Use the heck out of it! Get your hands dirty. Commit to the practices and then reflect on your experiences together. Something brought you here, so whatever it was, commit to that thing. Record your experiences in the spaces provided, talk about the parts that stand out for you, hear your partner share their thoughts and feelings as you go, and really lean into the potential to discover one another as you move through the pages ahead.

Be brave, be silly, be challenged, be naughty! Explore yourself - there is so much within you waiting for permission. Let this book be your permission to play.

CHAPTER 1.

COMMUNICATION IS SEXY

INTRODUCTION TO SEXUAL COMMUNICATION

Throughout this book, it will become very clear to you that the main ingredient to spicing up your sex life is communication. There is simply no way around it. In each practice offered and with every step you will take as a couple, you must first establish a solid foundation in communication. To put it simply, without communication, things can get messy very quickly. Communicating is the only way to stay connected through this journey together, so we must start here.

In this chapter, we will move through a series of practices that at first may not seem so sexy to the sexual adventurer ready to jump into this book. They may seem like more work than you're after, or perhaps a bit dull, a bit of a drag. "Active listening?" You may ask, "how is that erotic?"

I can assure you, however, that there is absolutely nothing sexier than proper communication because from here you can really dig into the depths of your pleasure, what *really* turns you on, and what you *really* want. Truly, what is sexier than being able to tell someone exactly what you want, to know exactly what they want, and really get to know your partner's sexual desires? What is dirty talk if not communication?

So, bear with me, explorers. I promise things will heat up very quickly if you're ready to lean into the journey with an open mind. Communication is extremely sexy if you're willing to go there.

1
ACTIVE LISTENING

The Active Listening practice is founded on the simple fact that in our fast-paced, power-focused society, we are taught in many ways how to speak but very seldom how to listen. We are taught debate tactics, how to use rhetoric, how to articulate, how to argue, and how to translate but never how to receive. Never how to listen. It is in listening, however, that we can really come to understand one another, how we can relate to one another, and how we can be relational.

THE PRACTICE

The practice itself is simple. Both partners sit facing one another, close enough that you could extend your arm and touch the other, but not so close that your body's touch.

Play a game of chance (e.g., rock, paper, scissors) to decide who will be the first speaker and who will be the first listener.

Decide on a prompting question, either from the examples below, or make up your own questions concerning your sexual self or your partnered sex life.

Set a timer for anywhere between five to ten minutes. The speaker will then spend the entirety of the set time in what we'll call "word vomit" mode; uninterrupted time to speak aloud anything that comes to mind in answering this question, or anything the question brings up for them that may or may not be directly related. The key word here is *uninterrupted*.

The role of the listening partner is to - well, listen. We often feel that adding little "mhmm's" and "uh-huh" responses while someone is speaking is helpful to the speaking party; it is our way of proving to the person that we are engaged and listening.

Most often, however, this is actually just to prove this to ourselves and adds nothing to the conversation. In fact, we are often so worried about proving that we are listening, that we forget to listen. In this exercise, the listening partner will stay completely silent while the speaker shares their talking. Really absorb what is said, regardless of where the speaker's train of thought leads. Do your best to follow, to really hear your partner until the time runs out.

When the time is up, switch roles. From here, you can decide whether the new speaker will be prompted by the same question as their partner, or whether the speaker will spend their time responding to what was said by their partner during the last round. Go back and forth at least a couple of times, so each partner has had at least two opportunities to speak.

PROMPTING QUESTIONS

- How was sex/sexuality viewed and discussed in your home as a child?

  _____

- How has your sexuality changed throughout your lifetime?

  _____

- Do you have a favorite sexual memory or story?

  _____

- What is your favorite thing about our sex life?

  _____

- When do you feel the most pleasure?

  _____

- What are some things you find yourself most attracted to in strangers?

  _____

- What are some of the things you find most attractive about me?

  _____

- Why do you want to spice up your/our sex life?

  _____

- What is your biggest fear?

  _____

RECORD & REFLECT

Here is your space to reflect on this practice as a couple.
Take some time, be honest, and answer truthfully.

What was the main takeaway/lesson from this practice?

_____

_____

_____

_____

What did you like about this practice?

_____

_____

_____

_____

What was most challenging about this practice?

_____

_____

_____

_____

RATE THIS PRACTICE:

BORING/UNPLEASANT				FINE/HELPFUL			INSPIRING/SUPER FUN		
1	2	3	4	5	6	7	8	9	10

2
ANY LITTLE THING

This practice acknowledges how hard it really is to be completely honest whenever someone asks us "What are you thinking?" Often, we sugarcoat our response, we offer only a small portion of the truth, we lie, or we simply say, "nothing, babe," and move on. Often, we do this either to protect the other, or because we feel that what we are thinking is insignificant, silly, embarrassing, or all of the above. On the contrary, however, often these silly little thoughts that happen in idle time are the most significant.

THE PRACTICE

For this practice, the couple will sit facing one another making eye contact in silence, until minds begin to wander. Eventually, they will; it is inevitable. Whatever comes to mind is to be spoken out loud, any little thing at all. Be brutally honest, throw out your filter, and share with your partner the first thing that comes to your mind.

After this, there isn't much structure in this practice, simply because it is so open-ended. Let things naturally flow from this initial prompt. Perhaps have a discussion or perhaps the other partner shares their thoughts without responding to the first speaker. See where this takes you. See how these seemingly "little" things can be unpacked in the context of your relationship, your shared experience. Where does your mind go in relation to the mind of your partner?

RECORD & REFLECT

Here is your space to reflect on this practice as a couple.
Take some time, be honest, and answer truthfully.

What was the main takeaway/lesson from this practice?

_____

_____

_____

_____

What did you like about this practice?

_____

_____

_____

_____

What was most challenging about this practice?

_____

_____

_____

_____

RATE THIS PRACTICE:

BORING/UNPLEASANT				FINE/HELPFUL			INSPIRING/SUPER FUN		
1	2	3	4	5	6	7	8	9	10

3
THREE AND THREE

This one requires you to get real, to get super honest. You're going to have to put your ego away for this one, so go into this knowing that you love one another, and this is all part of the process. Simply put, the *Three and Three Practice* asks each partner to think of three things they love that their partner does and three things they don't love so much.

THE PRACTICE

First, have this practice exist outside of your sex life and just apply it to your relationship as a whole. Do you love when your partner brings home your favorite ice cream? Do you love when they wait for you to watch the next episode? Do they make you swoon when they call you by a certain name? What are the things that stand out to you, that make you feel most loved?

Then, flip it. What do they do that just really irks you? Do they leave dirty dishes all over the counter? Are they always late? Are they hard to talk to about certain things? No one is perfect, and that is okay, but where can growth happen in your relationship?

Then, once you've gone through this practice outside of your sex life, apply the same practice to your sexual relationship. Share, one and then the other, three things you love either about sex itself, or specifically your sexual relationship, and three things you aren't crazy about, whether it be about sex itself (e.g., "I really just don't like anal play") or about your sexual relationship together (e.g., "I don't actually like it when you choke me"). It may feel challenging, to be honest about this part but see if you can trust your relationship enough to lean into this discomfort.

Afterwards, share some physical connection (hug or cuddle) and let feelings be felt if they come up. Talk them out and reflect on whether or not your ego is feeling threatened. It is challenging to be criticized, but doing so within a loving space is the yellow brick road to expansion.

RECORD & REFLECT

Here is your space to reflect on this practice as a couple.
Take some time, be honest, and answer truthfully.

What was the main takeaway/lesson from this practice?

_____

_____

_____

_____

What did you like about this practice?

_____

_____

_____

_____

What was most challenging about this practice?

_____

_____

_____

_____

RATE THIS PRACTICE:

BORING/UNPLEASANT				FINE/HELPFUL			INSPIRING/SUPER FUN		
1	2	3	4	5	6	7	8	9	10

4

ONE I LOVED, ONE TO CHANGE, ONE FOR NEXT TIME

This is a *Pillow-Talk Practice*, meaning it is most effective in the cuddly aftermath of sex. After you've had some good old-fashioned sexy time together, see if you can introduce this practice.

THE PRACTICE

Very simply, you'll both communicate one thing that you really loved from the sexual experience, one thing you would change about the experience and one idea or thing to try for next time.

This one is quite simple but allow it to open up some discussion. Allow it to be silly and embarrassing and giggly - communication doesn't have to be all serious all the time!

RECORD & REFLECT

Here is your space to reflect on this practice as a couple.
Take some time, be honest, and answer truthfully.

What was the main takeaway/lesson from this practice?

_____

_____

_____

_____

What did you like about this practice?

_____

_____

_____

_____

What was most challenging about this practice?

_____

_____

_____

_____

RATE THIS PRACTICE:

BORING/UNPLEASANT				FINE/HELPFUL			INSPIRING/SUPER FUN		
1	2	3	4	5	6	7	8	9	10

5

"WHAT I WANT"

Here, we unpack our discomfort in asking for what we want. Often, when things start to heat up, or when things have already gotten past this point right into the action, we find it hard, to be honest about what we want from our partner. We often have ideas in our minds that sound like "Oh, if he would just do this," or "I want her to wear this thing," or "I wish they would talk dirty to me," but we rarely feel confident being completely honest with these desires. We tend to go along with what our partner is doing, not wanting to hurt their feelings or kill the mood.

THE PRACTICE

With this practice, nothing will happen unless you ask for it, simple as that.

One partner sits, perhaps on the edge of a couch or a bed, and the other partner stands across the room. The concept is simple: The standing partner should approach the sitting partner. That's it.

The catch, however, is that the sitting partner has to instruct the standing partner every step of the way. Each move, each step, and each bit of clothing removed must be clearly asked for by the sitting partner until the standing partner has fully approached the sitter - whatever that means to you. (It could mean they are just in front of you, on top of you, or rubbing up on you; it's the sitter's choice!)

After that, the game can develop as you like. You can choose to keep the dynamic going or release the game once you and your partner have connected. However, the idea is that by starting with simple requests, you will develop the ability to clearly communicate what you want in a context removed from the heat and pressure of physical intimacy that's already underway.

Make sure to communicate boundaries before beginning this practice. We can't get into play if we are not fully able to relax. Agree on a safe word or a way to communicate prior to the practice so that if/when something doesn't feel right, you can respond accordingly.

And while I've encouraged moving through the discomfort and awkwardness and trying to lean into your partner's asks even if they're out of your comfort zone, there is a difference between this and forcing yourself into something that simply feels wrong.

Know your limits and play within them!

RECORD & REFLECT

Here is your space to reflect on this practice as a couple.
Take some time, be honest, and answer truthfully.

What was the main takeaway/lesson from this practice?

_____

_____

_____

_____

What did you like about this practice?

_____

_____

_____

_____

What was most challenging about this practice?

_____

_____

_____

_____

RATE THIS PRACTICE:

BORING/UNPLEASANT				FINE/HELPFUL			INSPIRING/SUPER FUN		
1	2	3	4	5	6	7	8	9	10

6
"LEND ME A HAND"

This is a chance to physically walk your partner through your personal pleasure. We can call it "assisted masturbation" if we like, and it sits somewhere in between the *Approach Me* Practice and the masturbation practices coming later in this book.

THE PRACTICE

The goal is to invite your partner into your masturbation routine, as though their hands were yours, and you will verbally guide them through what to do to you one step at a time. This is very different from foreplay, simply because their interaction with your body is not being guided by them and they are not striving to turn you on. They are, on the contrary, "lending you a hand" in turning yourself on. They're entering into your world.

You must be very specific to guide them through things exactly how you would do it, kind of like walking someone through how to knit or how to bait a hook. Make specific requests (examples below) from the very beginning to the very end, use toys if you usually use toys, and do your best to abandon any shame or embarrassment - let your freak flag fly! They're merely your assistant here; this is about you!

EXAMPLE GUIDANCE

- "Start by spreading my legs open, run your fingers up and down my inner thighs."

- "Put me in the shower and lather me with soap."

- "Very slowly, start to tickle around my labia. Lick your fingers or use lube."

- "Start by playing with my balls until I start to get hard."

- "Tease my clit with my dildo until I beg you to put it inside me."

- "Use one hand to stroke my cock and the other to tug on my balls."

- "Faster." Or "Harder."

- "Slower." Or "Don't stop."

PROMPTING QUESTIONS

- How was sex/sexuality viewed and discussed in your home as a child?

_____

- How has your sexuality changed throughout your lifetime?

_____

- Do you have a favorite sexual memory or story?

_____

- What is your favorite thing about our sex life?

_____

- When do you feel the most pleasure?

_____

- What are some things you find yourself most attracted to in strangers?

_____

- What are some of the things you find most attractive about me?

_____

- Why do you want to spice up your/our sex life?

_____

- What is your biggest fear?

_____

RECORD & REFLECT

Here is your space to reflect on this practice as a couple.
Take some time, be honest, and answer truthfully.

What was the main takeaway/lesson from this practice?

_____

_____

_____

_____

What did you like about this practice?

_____

_____

_____

_____

What was most challenging about this practice?

_____

_____

_____

_____

RATE THIS PRACTICE:

BORING/UNPLEASANT				FINE/HELPFUL			INSPIRING/SUPER FUN		
1	2	3	4	5	6	7	8	9	10

CHAPTER 2.

UNDERSTANDING EROTIC BLUEPRINTS

INTRODUCTION TO EROTIC BLUEPRINTS

This section is entirely derived from the work and teachings of Miss Jaiya Ma. We will apply her work to help us come to understand our unique turn-ons and personal pleasure.

Miss Jaiya Ma is an American somatic sexologist who coined the term and developed the conceptualization of Erotic Blueprints, which, to quote Jaiya herself, are offered as "a map of arousal that reveals your specific erotic language of orgasmic delight." In a nutshell, your Erotic Blueprint™ is the blueprint for how you get turned on, what turns you on, and how you most naturally and most intensely access pleasure. Jaiya boils this vast universe down into five main types within which all sexual humans exist, and from here one may learn about their type in hopes of understanding their pleasure more intimately.

Within relationships then, it is very helpful to understand your Erotic Blueprint as this allows a dialogue between partners regarding what type they know themselves to be and how they most easily access pleasure. It is just another way of communicating.

For the purpose of this book, we will explore practices for all five types, just because we can. We're spicing things up, aren't we? Do your best to lean into the practice that highlights each type as much as you can, like trying a new food or a new hairstyle - see how it feels to step outside the familiar and explore the other parts of yourself, and your partner!

If the two of you are different types, which is most common, explore one another's types, and then see how you can integrate both into your sex life. It can be playful and creative, and it's always fun to get to know yourself a little more intimately.

7

THE ENERGETIC: BREATHE WITH ME

The *Energetic* experience sexuality dominantly through energy, meaning they engage in sexuality through spirituality and find arousal in stimulation that goes beyond the physical into the energetic realm that cannot be seen with the naked eye. Rather, it must be felt. Below is a practice to help connect you to the experience of energetics in the bedroom.

THE PRACTICE

This one is very simple: the practice is to breathe together. We'll utilize what is known as the **Yab-Yum** position from Tantric Sexology.

The Yab-Yum is a partnered sitting position and can be manipulated in many ways to enhance comfort, contact, and pleasure. Have one partner sit comfortably with their legs out in front of them, bent at the knees and crossed either at the ankles or in a cross-legged posture.

This is traditionally the energetically masculine role. The other partner will then sit on the lap of the partner who is in the base position.

The person sitting on top (traditionally the feminine energy) will bend their knees to wrap their legs around the waist of their partner. Both parties may wrap their arms around the other in whatever way feels comfortable - usually, the person on top will wrap their arms around their partner's neck or shoulders, and the base partner's arms fit comfortably around the other's waist.

From here, gently place your foreheads together, close your eyes, and drop your awareness down into your breath.

Start to focus on synchronizing your breath, breathe together. You can interpret this as taking your inhales and exhales at the same time, or you can alternate, so that when one partner inhales the other exhales, and vice versa.

The first option offers more of a platonic energy, two individuals colliding in time and space. The latter option generates more of a unified, singular experience between the bodies involved - that of giving and receiving.

This method is often used for building sexual energy, as the cycle of the unified breath moves energy continuously into one body and then out and into the other. If this method interests you, try incorporating visualization as well. Picture this energy moving into you and then out of you and into your partner in this same way.

Allow this to be the entirety of the practice but stay open to whatever experience builds from it.

RECORD & REFLECT

Here is your space to reflect on this practice as a couple.
Take some time, be honest, and answer truthfully.

What was the main takeaway/lesson from this practice?

_____

_____

_____

_____

What did you like about this practice?

_____

_____

_____

_____

What was most challenging about this practice?

_____

_____

_____

_____

RATE THIS PRACTICE:

BORING/UNPLEASANT				FINE/HELPFUL			INSPIRING/SUPER FUN		
1	2	3	4	5	6	7	8	9	10

8
THE SENSUAL: THE FIVE SENSES

The *Sensual* experiences sexuality dominantly through the senses. While this may seem like an oxymoron because sex appears to always be experienced through the senses in one way or another, for the Sensual, sexuality is all about sensuality and stimulation of the senses through setting the right mood and heating things up one sense at a time, with equal attention to each.

THE PRACTICE

For the sensual, we'll aim to involve all of the senses in the setting of the mood.

Choose which partner is being romanced, and who will do the romancing. Then, whoever is doing the romancing gets to get creative. Consider one sense at a time (sight, sound, taste, smell, touch) and come up with a way to appeal to that sense in your partner. Introduce one sense at a time, leaving touch for last, until you build up to a fully encompassing sensory experience with all senses involved. When the mood is fully set, explore where a touch can take you.

FOR EXAMPLE:

Perhaps you dim the lights and light a few scented candles and slip into your sexiest silk. This stimulates both sight and smell. You play the type of music that you know turns your partner on, or maybe there is no music, and you decide to talk a little dirty instead.

That covers sound. You feed your partner some super juicy strawberries, or maybe they get to suck on your fingers instead. Lastly, you have them lie down and offer a slow, sensual massage. Or perhaps they get to touch by running their hands up and down your body and feeling the silk against your skin.

RECORD & REFLECT

Here is your space to reflect on this practice as a couple.
Take some time, be honest, and answer truthfully.

What was the main takeaway/lesson from this practice?

_____

_____

_____

_____

What did you like about this practice?

_____

_____

_____

_____

What was most challenging about this practice?

_____

_____

_____

_____

RATE THIS PRACTICE:

BORING/UNPLEASANT				FINE/HELPFUL			INSPIRING/SUPER FUN		
1	2	3	4	5	6	7	8	9	10

9

THE KINK:
SEX SHOPPING

For the *Kink*, it's just about spicing things up, stepping outside the box, and getting a little freaky. While many of us read "kink" and think in extremes, the kink can mean a very wide range of things, with the boiled-down definition of kink being simply to be turned on by the taboo.

THE PRACTICE

Let's get out of the house for this one, go to the sex shop!

Literally - go on an outing together to the sex shop and see what inspires you. Once you get to the shop, you can choose to either separate and pick up a couple of things each to reconvene after you've browsed alone, or you can move through the store together.

No matter which choice you make, it's important to notice how different things make you feel while moving around the store.

Do you notice an instant sensation when you look at certain things? Do other things intimidate you? Do particular sections inspire your fantasies? How does it feel to imagine the uses for all of the different pleasure products?

Chose some things together to bring home and try them out!

RECORD & REFLECT

Here is your space to reflect on this practice as a couple.
Take some time, be honest, and answer truthfully.

What was the main takeaway/lesson from this practice?

_____

_____

_____

_____

What did you like about this practice?

_____

_____

_____

_____

What was most challenging about this practice?

_____

_____

_____

_____

RATE THIS PRACTICE:

BORING/UNPLEASANT				FINE/HELPFUL			INSPIRING/SUPER FUN		
1	2	3	4	5	6	7	8	9	10

10
THE SEXUAL:
SHUT UP AND SEX

The *Sexual* experiences sexual arousal in a very literal sense, they like to get straight to the point - they just love sex! The Sexual doesn't need all the bells and whistles to get down and dirty; they're here for the tried-and-true intercourse itself. They like to keep it straight to the point. But this doesn't mean they aren't up for a little fun!

THE PRACTICE

For the Sexual, we're not worried about the energies in the space or all of the sensory stimulation. We're focused on the sex, the genitals, and the hot and heavy contact.

Simply, grab your partner and have sex! That's the whole practice! The catch, however, is that you're not going to speak to one another the entire time. From beginning to finish, it's all in the act, in the body, and you must therefore use body language to communicate the whole way through.

For a little added challenge, you could even try covering both of your mouths (with tape, or maybe a gag-ball) and see how this spices things up even more, and then go at it! Get all touchy-feely and handsy, get physical!

RECORD & REFLECT

Here is your space to reflect on this practice as a couple.
Take some time, be honest, and answer truthfully.

What was the main takeaway/lesson from this practice?

_____

_____

_____

_____

What did you like about this practice?

_____

_____

_____

_____

What was most challenging about this practice?

_____

_____

_____

_____

RATE THIS PRACTICE:

BORING/UNPLEASANT				FINE/HELPFUL			INSPIRING/SUPER FUN		
1	2	3	4	5	6	7	8	9	10

11

THE SHAPESHIFTER: WILD CARD

The *Shapeshifter* is here for it all; they can just get into whatever their partner is into with equal enthusiasm in all sorts of sexual scenarios.

The Shapeshifter has a little bit of each type within them, and because of this, they can find pleasure from many different sources. They are very versatile lovers.

THE PRACTICE

For the shapeshifter, there can be a lot of fun in not knowing what they're going to get and the continuous exploration of the various forms of sexuality within themselves.

Choose who will be the seducer and who will be the seduced for this practice. The seducer will then choose one of the other four types (the Energetic, the Sensual, the Sexual, the Kink) to explore, and will not tell their partner which they have chosen.

The seducer will then go forth with seducing their partner through targeting the type they have chosen (try to use a method you haven't used before), and in response, the partner being seduced will receive the seduction being offered, until they have been able to recognize which type is being explored. Go along with this type for a while, and then, without verbally expressing it, switch roles.

The partner initially being seduced will become the seducer, will choose a different type to target (the Energetic, the Sensual, the Sexual, the Kink), and will begin to lead their partner through a new experience without breaking the energy.

The types will flow seamlessly into one another, in an exploration of how it is possible to dance from one into another in a single experience.

RECORD & REFLECT

Here is your space to reflect on this practice as a couple.
Take some time, be honest, and answer truthfully.

What was the main takeaway/lesson from this practice?

_____

_____

_____

_____

What did you like about this practice?

_____

_____

_____

_____

What was most challenging about this practice?

_____

_____

_____

_____

RATE THIS PRACTICE:

BORING/UNPLEASANT				FINE/HELPFUL			INSPIRING/SUPER FUN		
1	2	3	4	5	6	7	8	9	10

CHAPTER 3.

MASTURBATION

INTRODUCTION TO MASTURBATION

Your primary sexual relationship must always be the sexual relationship you have with yourself. In the wise words of Ru Paul, "*If you can't love yourself, how the hell are you gonna love somebody else?*" And that's just the damn truth. You cannot expect your partner to be responsible for your pleasure. Getting to know your pleasure is something you must explore with yourself, and then you must continue to nurture your solo sexuality throughout your partnership and partnered sex journey.

It is extremely important to carve out time and energy for sex with yourself, to maintain a dialogue with your pleasure as it evolves and grows in the same way that your partnered sexual relationship will evolve and grow over time. Recognize these different relationships as equally important and as crucial for the expansion of the other. To have great sex with your partner is to know how to f*ck yourself, where your pleasures lay, and who you are as a sexual being, and then to f*ck yourself is to show up ready to bring that pleasure to your partner.

Below are some practices for developing a more consistent, explorative, playful, intentional masturbation practice. Know that masturbation is crucial for not only sexual health but overall health and wellness on a long-term scale. Take pride in your sex life with yourself and prioritize your pleasure in your own body. Love yourself!

12
ROMANCE YOURSELF

While this may sound quite simple, it is very rare that we ever take the time and energy to love ourselves in the way we love our partners.

If our primary sexual relationship is with ourselves, then our primary romantic relationships must also be with our incredible selves, and once again, these relationships must be nourished and prioritized as the most important relationship in our entire lives.

THE PRACTICE

What does it look like to romance yourself? Many of us will find this quite challenging to visualize. So, let's start with something easier: What does it look like for you to dedicate an evening to romancing your partner? Perhaps you dress in something a little sexy, perhaps you cook a nice meal or order their favorite food, perhaps you run them a bath, light a candle, play their favorite music - what are those things that come to mind when you want to spoil your loved one?

Now, pick an evening to get romantic, but this time the person you're romancing is you! So, consider what it means to you to be romanced, how would your dream evening of luxury and pleasure go? Down to the last detail, as though you wanted everything to go perfectly for a lover.

And don't cut corners just because it's for yourself! Don't just opt for the oversized t-shirt and sweats you've been wearing all day because no one's there to see you in all your sexy glory - YOU are your primary lover. YOU deserve to revel in your own beauty. Go all out on yourself and indulge. You deserve it!

Move slowly through the stages of the evening, whatever you've planned for yourself. Then, if the mood is right, go ahead and make love to yourself while you're at it. The cherry on top!

RECORD & REFLECT

Here is your space to reflect on this practice as a couple.
Take some time, be honest, and answer truthfully.

What was the main takeaway/lesson from this practice?

_____

_____

_____

_____

What did you like about this practice?

_____

_____

_____

_____

What was most challenging about this practice?

_____

_____

_____

_____

RATE THIS PRACTICE:

BORING/UNPLEASANT				FINE/HELPFUL			INSPIRING/SUPER FUN		
1	2	3	4	5	6	7	8	9	10

13

"I MADE THIS FOR YOU"

Equally important to nurturing your own solo sex life, is to encourage and support your partner's solo sex life.

Your sex lives with yourselves allow you to come together with new creative ideas and remain inspired within your partnered sex. So, how can we encourage our partner's masturbation in a healthy, creative way?

THE PRACTICE

Again, you're setting the full mood as you did for yourself in the previous exercise, but this time you're creating the scene for your partner instead of yourself, and you won't be there when they get to enjoy it.

Wait until you'll have some time alone at home to set things up just right for them, and then set the stage for them to walk into and get fully immersed in the sexy vibes without you there.

Some ideas could be a scavenger hunt, a note or set of instructions, or perhaps even a recorded message that you could send to their phone explaining the situation to them. Maybe you can leave a new sex toy on their bed for them to try, maybe you can run them a bath or cue up their favorite movie, or leave them some sexy photos of yourself to find.

Whatever it is, the goal is to encourage their solo sexy time, so make it unique to them. Think about the things they like to do when they're indulging, or perhaps things they never do for themselves. Then offer it to them, and let them sink into it, alone!

RECORD & REFLECT

Here is your space to reflect on this practice as a couple.
Take some time, be honest, and answer truthfully.

What was the main takeaway/lesson from this practice?

_____

_____

_____

_____

What did you like about this practice?

_____

_____

_____

_____

What was most challenging about this practice?

_____

_____

_____

_____

RATE THIS PRACTICE:

BORING/UNPLEASANT				FINE/HELPFUL			INSPIRING/SUPER FUN		
1	2	3	4	5	6	7	8	9	10

14
EROTIC MEDITATION

This one might sound a little intimidating if you're not someone that already has an established meditation practice. This practice can also quite possibly overlap with the category of Audioporn, depending on what you're into. However, I will maintain that erotic meditation is very much its own category of erotica as well as its own form of meditation, existing at the intersection of sexuality and spirituality, so we must approach it in this intentional way.

Simply, an erotic meditation is a guided meditation that stimulates your pleasure. It is approached as any other meditation, in a still body, either seated or laying down, and is entered into through the breath.

THE PRACTICE

There are tons and tons of erotic meditations online if one simply searches in their browser. It may take a bit of trial and error before you find one that works well for you. Sometimes it comes down to just finding one that has a voice you like, or perhaps you prefer to focus more on breathing than on visualization - give a few a shot before you find your niche.

Once you've selected a meditation, find a comfortable space where you will not be disturbed for a while. Either find a comfortable seat or lay down on your back. Enter into meditation as you would any other meditation and do your best to focus on your stillness. Commonly, sensations will occur in the body, and very often we will find ourselves growing more and more aroused throughout the meditation. That is just fine but try to refrain from masturbation until the end of the meditation. See how you can let your desire build as you remain in stillness before you give into your pleasure.

If you feel called to masturbate after your meditation, then see how it feels to enter into meditation again, post orgasm, and meditate on the pleasure you've just felt.

RECORD & REFLECT

Here is your space to reflect on this practice as a couple.
Take some time, be honest, and answer truthfully.

What was the main takeaway/lesson from this practice?

_____

_____

_____

_____

What did you like about this practice?

_____

_____

_____

_____

What was most challenging about this practice?

_____

_____

_____

_____

RATE THIS PRACTICE:

BORING/UNPLEASANT				FINE/HELPFUL			INSPIRING/SUPER FUN		
1	2	3	4	5	6	7	8	9	10

15
SOLO MIRROR GAZING

How often do we take the time not just to glance in the mirror to check our outfit or make sure nothing's in our teeth, but to spend time looking at ourselves, seeing ourselves, and recognizing ourselves in our bodies, exactly as we are? How often, by contrast, do we spend time admiring our partner, checking them out, giving them the old up-and-down, and glancing lovingly at them across the room?

It's time to admire ourselves, sex life spicer-uppers. It's time to gaze into the mirror.

THE PRACTICE

While it may seem easy, this challenge can be one of the most difficult in this whole book. In essence, I'm asking you to stand in front of the mirror (a large enough mirror that you can see the majority of your body), nude, and look at yourself. In this simplicity, it's easy.

It's difficult, however, because we're not taught how to look at ourselves lovingly; we're not taught how to love ourselves. We're taught to be very critical of our appearance, so naturally, the first things that will come up in a pro-longed period of staring at ourselves will be the criticisms, the things we dislike, and the imperfections.

I encourage you to push through these things. Let them come up, don't fight them, but then move past them, and know that these voices are not truths, but rather constructed opinions created by a world that fears love.

Start by trying to find one thing you like in your reflection. What's your best feature, in your opinion? Then see if you can find another. And then another. See how many you can find, no matter how small or seemingly insignificant. Perhaps you like a specific freckle, perhaps it's your hair color, or perhaps you have a cute belly button.

RECORD & REFLECT

Here is your space to reflect on this practice as a couple.
Take some time, be honest, and answer truthfully.

What was the main takeaway/lesson from this practice?

_____

_____

_____

_____

What did you like about this practice?

_____

_____

_____

_____

What was most challenging about this practice?

_____

_____

_____

_____

RATE THIS PRACTICE:

BORING/UNPLEASANT				FINE/HELPFUL			INSPIRING/SUPER FUN		
1	2	3	4	5	6	7	8	9	10

16
PARTNERED MIRROR GAZING

This is similar to the previous *Solo Mirror Gazing* practice, but this time we're involving our partners.

THE PRACTICE

Both partners will stand in front of the mirror (a large enough mirror that you can see the majority of your bodies), nude, one behind the other but without the view of the mirror obstructed. The partner standing closest to the mirror, in front of the other person, will do their mirror gazing at themselves, and the partner standing behind will do their mirror gazing at their partner in front of them.

The partner standing behind will find the things in the reflection that they like about their partner in front of them, whatever they may be, no matter how small or seemingly insignificant, and they will say these things out loud.

FOR EXAMPLE:

"I like your smile lines," "You have such strong thighs," "You have beautiful hands," "I love your eyelashes," and so on. Just keep saying them out loud as they come to you, as you look at your partner through the mirror standing before you. Be as open and as honest as possible and keep going until you've mentioned everything in detail.

Avoid saying things like "I just love all of you," or "Your whole body is amazing," as these types of generalized comments don't require the same amount of intention and awareness of your partner's unique being. Once you've completed your gazing of one partner, switch roles.

RECORD & REFLECT

Here is your space to reflect on this practice as a couple.
Take some time, be honest, and answer truthfully.

What was the main takeaway/lesson from this practice?

_____

_____

_____

_____

What did you like about this practice?

_____

_____

_____

_____

What was most challenging about this practice?

_____

_____

_____

_____

RATE THIS PRACTICE:

BORING/UNPLEASANT				FINE/HELPFUL			INSPIRING/SUPER FUN		
1	2	3	4	5	6	7	8	9	10

17
MIRROR
MASTURBATION

How well do you know your sexual self? How long have you spent watching yourself have sex? Have you ever witnessed yourself having sex with yourself? How close are you with your genitals? We're getting nice and intimate with this one!

THE PRACTICE

For this round, we're right up and personal with our mirrors. Yep, we're going to watch ourselves masturbate! This might seem cringey at first, but then why don't we want to see ourselves? After all, we love watching our partners, don't we? Aren't you - your own primary partner?

Find a comfortable position where you can position a mirror so that you may watch yourself when you get going and really see your entire body in view at once in the reflection. Ideally, you can sit in front of the mirror or lie down, to maximize ease.

Once you start to get all up on yourself, try your best to keep your eyes on yourself and watch your body, from genitals to eye contact with your reflection. Try to push through any discomfort that comes with seeing yourself like this, step into the role of your own lover, your sexual self, separate from your critical self, and welcome this sexual version of you into your experience.

RECORD & REFLECT

Here is your space to reflect on this practice as a couple.
Take some time, be honest, and answer truthfully.

What was the main takeaway/lesson from this practice?

_____

_____

_____

_____

What did you like about this practice?

_____

_____

_____

_____

What was most challenging about this practice?

_____

_____

_____

_____

RATE THIS PRACTICE:

BORING/UNPLEASANT				FINE/HELPFUL			INSPIRING/SUPER FUN		
1	2	3	4	5	6	7	8	9	10

18
MUTUAL MASTURBATION

Now that we've established a pretty solid relationship with our solo sexual selves, it's time to include our partner in our masturbation practice. While we've discussed thus far how important it is to learn to be with yourself as a sexual being, it can also be very explorative and playful to invite your partner into your space, where it's still you and your body, but they can share in this space with you.

THE PRACTICE

Masturbate, together! Get into a comfy, sexy space, perhaps the bedroom or the shower, where you both feel at ease and natural. Use whatever toys or methods of masturbation you usually feel called to when alone, and then get down to business.

The fun part is to try to pay attention to your partner as you pleasure yourself. Try not to break eye contact, or if you do, keep your eyes on your partner in some way - on another part of their body or watch as they move around.

Remember that you're still masturbating, so keep things separate from one another physically, but find that connection in observing your partner's pleasure in watching you and being watched by you. It can be so hot to witness how your lover loves themself!

RECORD & REFLECT

Here is your space to reflect on this practice as a couple.
Take some time, be honest, and answer truthfully.

What was the main takeaway/lesson from this practice?

_____

_____

_____

_____

What did you like about this practice?

_____

_____

_____

_____

What was most challenging about this practice?

_____

_____

_____

_____

RATE THIS PRACTICE:

BORING/UNPLEASANT				FINE/HELPFUL			INSPIRING/SUPER FUN		
1	2	3	4	5	6	7	8	9	10

CHAPTER 4.

DIRTY TALK

INTRODUCTION TO DIRTY TALK

Dirty Talk is one of those things that can be hard to take seriously when doing it ourselves. Realistically, almost all of us love dirty talk when we're on the receiving end, but it can be quite daunting to be the one spitting the goods. It's kind of like when we hear our own voice on a recording—we tend to make ourselves cringe!

The reason for this cringing, why we find it hard to take ourselves seriously, is because we struggle to recognize our desirability. When our partner starts to dirty talk, we find it sexy and exciting because we find them sexy and exciting; we find them desirable. With ourselves, however, if we've never recognized ourselves as equally sexy and exciting, equally desirable, then to hear ourselves trying to dirty talk feels cringey and silly, and we often wind up just giving up altogether.

Well, firstly, let me remind you that sex isn't meant to be all serious all the time. It's okay to get a bit silly and giggly when trying new things; it's part of the experience. Sex is play!

Second, recognize that your partner is with you because they desire you, just as much as you desire them. Just as sexy and exciting as you think they are; they see this in you too. Trust me, you're hot! And your partner wants to hear you, confident and dirty, expressing your desires to them, like you haven't a doubt in your mind what you want and how you want it.

So, use these following practices to explore dirty talk in a playful, yet intentional, way. Be silly and have fun but try to get past the cringe phase and discover how it feels to stand confidently in your dirty-talking persona. I promise they're inside of you, you just might have to give them a push!

19

"WHAT I'M GONNA DO TO YOU"

Dirty talk is simply a way of turning our partners on with our words, and this can be done before sex, using our words as foreplay, or as added stimulation during sex itself. For this practice, we're going to see how some dirty talk can be used as foreplay and how horny can you get your partner without even touching them.

THE PRACTICE

Get into the same space but be far enough away from one another that you are not physically touching (perhaps across the room, or on opposite sides of the couch). Make sure you have a clear, unobstructed view of one another.

Choose who will be the seducer, and who will be the seduced. The seducer, maintaining eye contact with their partner throughout the entire practice, is going to start listing, in chronological order, all of the things they are going to do to their partner, once the practice is over. Be creative with it, but also be very literal and detailed in your speech.

FOR EXAMPLE:

"I'm going to walk across this room slowly, and you'll think I'm planning to approach you from the front, but I'll take you in my arms from behind. I'll place one hand gently around your neck, and slide my other hand down your chest, under your shirt, and I'll tilt your head to the side as I start to kiss your neck."

Lots of detail, lots of time to build. See how crazy you can drive yourselves with just your words, and then when you're ready, switch roles.

RECORD & REFLECT

Here is your space to reflect on this practice as a couple.
Take some time, be honest, and answer truthfully.

What was the main takeaway/lesson from this practice?

_____

_____

_____

_____

What did you like about this practice?

_____

_____

_____

_____

What was most challenging about this practice?

_____

_____

_____

_____

RATE THIS PRACTICE:

BORING/UNPLEASANT				FINE/HELPFUL			INSPIRING/SUPER FUN		
1	2	3	4	5	6	7	8	9	10

20
"I LOVE IT WHEN YOU..."

This one can be introduced once things have already started to kick into action, during any stage of a sexual encounter. This one is all about recognizing how good it feels when our partner lets us know when they like something that we're doing when we are pleasuring them. It's important to receive a little validation here and there, and also to know when you're on the right track.

It's just all about that praise, 'bout that praise, no struggle.

THE PRACTICE

This doesn't have to be practiced in any formal time frame or structure. It can be something you can introduce as much or as little as you wish once you get more comfortable with it, but it's good to start introducing it with clear intention and focus, so you can get the hang of things.

Simply, when starting into sexy time with your partner, see if you can verbally let them know every time that they do something you really like. The key is to be specific, and literal, with your words. Don't be afraid of sexy vocabulary - use all those dirty words that come into your mind, and don't sugarcoat things!

FOR EXAMPLE:

"I love it when you use your hands and your mouth on me at the same time," "I love it when you stroke my cock slow and hard," or "I love it when you grind your clit against me."

RECORD & REFLECT

Here is your space to reflect on this practice as a couple.
Take some time, be honest, and answer truthfully.

What was the main takeaway/lesson from this practice?

_____

_____

_____

_____

What did you like about this practice?

_____

_____

_____

_____

What was most challenging about this practice?

_____

_____

_____

_____

RATE THIS PRACTICE:

BORING/UNPLEASANT				FINE/HELPFUL			INSPIRING/SUPER FUN		
1	2	3	4	5	6	7	8	9	10

21
TALK IN ACTION

Now that we've established somewhat of an ability to use our voice during sex, let's see how far we can push it.

This practice operates on the premise that during sex we are almost always thinking something or having thoughts, most of which we keep to ourselves, and it's time to let it all out! By taking that extra mile, removing the filter on our voice, this practice will probably get quite silly, and very dirty, all at the same time.

THE PRACTICE

Talk In Action is to literally try and talk throughout the entirety of a sexual experience with your partner. From start to finish, see if you can keep talking the whole time.

Not just about anything - we're not discussing taxes or when to pick the children up or what we're having for dinner.

We're still staying focused, talking about the sex at hand, and remaining very present in our bodies. However, anything that comes to mind during the act, we're letting it all out.

This can be a combination of various types of communication, from instructions ("Move your leg over a little," "F*ck me harder," or "Slow down"), to feedback ("Yes, like that, babe," "I liked it better when you…," "I'm not loving this," or "You look so hot when you do that"), to dirty talk and kink (whatever dynamic there is, dirty names, make them beg for certain things, etc.) - it can go anywhere. the point is to keep it coming, to let it all flow out of you.

RECORD & REFLECT

Here is your space to reflect on this practice as a couple.
Take some time, be honest, and answer truthfully.

What was the main takeaway/lesson from this practice?

_____

_____

_____

_____

What did you like about this practice?

_____

_____

_____

_____

What was most challenging about this practice?

_____

_____

_____

_____

RATE THIS PRACTICE:

BORING/UNPLEASANT				FINE/HELPFUL			INSPIRING/SUPER FUN		
1	2	3	4	5	6	7	8	9	10

22
PHONE SEX

Phone sex is fun because it combines both masturbation and dirty talk.

This is also why it can be quite challenging. It requires a level of comfort between yourself and your partner that must first be established through learning how to access both of these practices separately (masturbation and dirty talk) and then leaning into both, together, and creating an entirely new space.

It can be giggly or feel silly at first, just like them all, but I guarantee when you get past the giggles there is a playful, very sexy world that awaits you.

It is also important to recognize *Phone Sex* as separate from *Sexting*, though they can be combined.

THE PRACTICE

If there is a time when you and your partner are not together for a night or a period of time, this is the time to try *Phone Sex*.

Maybe there's a moment where you're already feeling in the mood, maybe you're fresh out of the shower or you're lying there in bed late at night, or maybe you're just thinking of your boo. Give them a call and tell them what's on your mind.

Be descriptive about where you are and what you'd want them to do to you (or what you'd want to do to them) if they were there with you in this moment. Slowly, the vibes can start to build.

Start to introduce some instructions. Maybe you ask them if they're wearing a shirt, and then you tell them to take it off. Maybe you tell them to spread their legs so they can touch themselves for you like you would touch them if you were there. Use your imagination, but be communicative, and most importantly, really follow the instructions you receive, really get into it!

Try not to laugh it off or merely humor them for their own pleasure, indulge in your pleasure too!

This is a great way to stay connected in long-distance relationships, or even during short separations so that when you come back together you can really live out all the things you discussed on the phone.

RECORD & REFLECT

Here is your space to reflect on this practice as a couple.
Take some time, be honest, and answer truthfully.

What was the main takeaway/lesson from this practice?

_____

_____

_____

_____

What did you like about this practice?

_____

_____

_____

_____

What was most challenging about this practice?

_____

_____

_____

_____

RATE THIS PRACTICE:

BORING/UNPLEASANT				FINE/HELPFUL			INSPIRING/SUPER FUN		
1	2	3	4	5	6	7	8	9	10

23
SEXTING

Not to be confused with *Phone Sex,* though they can go hand in hand, or one can perhaps lead on to the other. While phone sex is done through a phone conversation in real-time, sexting is all through writing. Then, it's a creative writing exercise!

THE PRACTICE

This is your chance to try writing short-form erotica for your babe, so you can be as poetic and lengthy or as short and to the point as you wish. "Sexting" refers simply to sending sexy text messages, so this can be interpreted in whatever "sexy messages" means to you, but the challenge is to initiate the dirty chat and then stick with it.

You can initiate with something as simple as "I'm thinking about you," or you can get as elaborate and poetic as you'd like. Try to build it into a detailed, sexy conversation, rather than just leaving it at the surface level with dead-end messages.

FOR EXAMPLE:

In reply to "I'm thinking of you," you could say, "what specifically are you thinking about?" To which could be replied, "I'm thinking about how you looked this morning with nothing but your towel wrapped around your waist," and then, "and how does that make you feel?"

And so on. Keep building, keep asking questions, more or less like an improv game. The more open-ended the question, the better, because this will allow the dirty messages to get more and more creative.

If you feel called to it, you can start to send photos or perhaps you can start to masturbate and describe exactly what you're doing to your partner. The possibilities are endless!

RECORD & REFLECT

Here is your space to reflect on this practice as a couple.
Take some time, be honest, and answer truthfully.

What was the main takeaway/lesson from this practice?

_____

_____

_____

_____

What did you like about this practice?

_____

_____

_____

_____

What was most challenging about this practice?

_____

_____

_____

_____

RATE THIS PRACTICE:

BORING/UNPLEASANT				FINE/HELPFUL			INSPIRING/SUPER FUN		
1	2	3	4	5	6	7	8	9	10

CHAPTER 5.

FOREPLAY

INTRODUCTION TO FOREPLAY

Foreplay is one of those challenging things to define because the reality is that for many, what's considered to be "foreplay" is really sex itself. The concept of foreplay refers to the things we do to get into the mood for sex, to get turned on, to make us want the sex itself - which most commonly refers to penetrative sex.

The issue here is that this concept of foreplay, when looked at as the "lead-up" to sex being everything other than penetration, is inherently heterosexual and only works when penetrative sex is on the table. For the sake of these practices then, foreplay will refer still to the tactics and practices we use to set the mood and turn our partner on, but we will expand past simply the physical acts of foreplay possible in recognition that all forms of sex are foreplay, and all forms of foreplay are also sex.

So, let these practices be a guide for you to start being a bit more intentional about prioritizing foreplay, but start to think of it all as foreplay, as setting the mood, as getting into the zone, as turning each other on in your relationship. Think of when your partner does the dishes for you as foreplay, of when you laugh together as foreplay, of when you wear their favorite shirt of yours as foreplay. Think of your relationship as constantly in the act of foreplay because you are constantly in the creation of a relationship that inspires sexual desire, and this begins way before you even get into the bedroom.

It is also important to note, in reference back to our discussion of Erotic Blueprints, that some of us can enter right into sex without any build-up, but many of us need time and space to get into our bodies in this way. There is an old saying, "Where men's arousal is quick and all at once, like lighting a match, women's arousal is like bringing water to a boil." Some bodies need to receive that slow build, whereas others can just snap right into it. Make space for this and recognize the differences in anatomy and pleasure. Foreplay allows more play!

24
SETTING THE MOOD

The most basic act of foreplay is setting the proper mood to help you both get into the zone, and this can be very simple, or very elaborate, depending on what you prefer, or perhaps what pushes you a little outside of your comfort zone together.

Setting the mood can mean something different to everyone, but there are definitely some universal ideas that pop into our minds when we think of "setting the mood" that may feel a tad clichéd or cheesy.

Well, they may clichéd, but they're considered clichéd because they work. It's okay to be a little cheesy now and again; deep down we all love that cheesy stuff, no matter how much we hate to admit it. Who better to get into the cheese with than the person you love most?

THE PRACTICE

Choose an evening when you both have lots of time and enough energy to be fully present together without any time constraints or too much yawning.

This is important, because the main thing that prevents us from getting fully indulgent in mood setting most of the time, is simply the lack of time and energy to do so.

Make sure you can both show up ready to get right into it, to go that extra mile, to put in that extra bit of effort that makes all the difference.

Then, build your scene together, from the ground up. Start by brainstorming together, maybe make a list, of things that come to mind for both of you when you think of "setting the mood."

Maybe a particular kind of music, some rose petals, a nice bath, or maybe you're designing a sex room in your head with apparatuses hanging from the rafters.

Whatever comes to mind in thinking of setting the mood, share it with your partner, and add it to the list. Share your wildest dreams, your most sexy dream scene.

Then, within your means, create this collaborative experience together. Make sure you're pulling ideas from both partners equally to create an equally pleasurable scene for both of you.

And this can get quite abstract, so have fun with it and lean into the silliness if it starts to get a tad theatrical.

Maybe you're going out shopping together for ingredients to make your favorite meal, maybe you're just serving chocolate-covered strawberries and champagne, maybe you're skipping the food and getting right into sexy time, or maybe you're laying out a museum of dildos.

Whatever this looks like, take the time to pull all the stops. Shower the bed in rose petals or dollar bills, candles burning, sexy R&B playing.

Indulge in your setting of the mood as you would spend all your energy trying to turn your partner on during traditional foreplay. Turn each other on with the ambiance.

Let the journey of creating this scene be equally as sensual, playful, kinky, and naughty as the sex that may follow. And then you can get freaky!

RECORD & REFLECT

Here is your space to reflect on this practice as a couple.
Take some time, be honest, and answer truthfully.

What was the main takeaway/lesson from this practice?

_____

_____

_____

_____

What did you like about this practice?

_____

_____

_____

_____

What was most challenging about this practice?

_____

_____

_____

_____

RATE THIS PRACTICE:

BORING/UNPLEASANT		FINE/HELPFUL		INSPIRING/SUPER FUN	
1 2 3 4		5 6 7		8 9 10	

25
DANCE WITH ME

For those of you that read the title of this practice and said, "I can't dance," it is extra important that you give this one a go.

Dancing is the most direct and simplest way to get out of our heads and into our bodies if we let it be. The struggle with dancing is that we have been taught that it is supposed to look a certain way, that our bodies have to be able to move in a specific way to specific music, for our movements to be considered "dancing."

This is a fat slice of bologna, my friends. Literally, everybody, *every single body*, can dance.

Like every other practice thus far, it starts with abandoning the fear. How do we release fear? We find some aspect of comfort, something we can settle into, something familiar and safe. In this practice, this comfort, this safety, will be your partner.

THE PRACTICE

Slip into something really comfortable, anything at all that makes you feel comfortable in your body. You can be butt naked, in your PJs, in some sexy lingerie, in your boxers - whatever makes you feel liberated and sexy and comfortable.

Find a space with enough room to move; maybe your kitchen or your living room, maybe outside on the lawn or in a park.

Turn on some music that makes you both feel really sensual and naughty, and dance! You can start individually, dancing separately, to try and get into the swing of things. Often it helps to close your eyes when you're first trying to get into your body. Closing the eyes will remove the awareness of anyone else around you and will help you silence your mind. Sink into your own world.

Then, when it feels natural, see if the two of you can connect. Maybe grab hands or one another by the waist, whatever comes naturally, and see if you can move together. See if you can take turns leading, moving your bodies in sync with one another, and reading one another's body language.

Visualize that there is no one else in the world, that it's just the two of you, at this moment, making love with your bodies to the music. Explore different types of movement. Crawl around on the floor, roll over one another, lift one another up and spin around, sway, grind, shake, bounce! Let the movement be your pleasure, pleasure one another with your movement.

Let dance be foreplay; let dance be sex!

RECORD & REFLECT

Here is your space to reflect on this practice as a couple.
Take some time, be honest, and answer truthfully.

What was the main takeaway/lesson from this practice?

_____

_____

_____

_____

What did you like about this practice?

_____

_____

_____

_____

What was most challenging about this practice?

_____

_____

_____

_____

RATE THIS PRACTICE:

BORING/UNPLEASANT				FINE/HELPFUL			INSPIRING/SUPER FUN		
1	2	3	4	5	6	7	8	9	10

26
TANTRIC KISSING

Tantric Kissing is derived from the ancient Tantric Yoga Philosophy and comes from a rich lineage of sexuality practices and modality that focuses on sexuality as an embodied, spiritual practice.

To practice sex in a tantric way means to develop a deep connection with your body and your senses, and to use mindfulness to engage in pleasure both solo and with your partner.

The tantric kiss, then, is to kiss with your whole body and soul.

THE PRACTICE

First, get into a comfy position together, deeply intertwined with one another's bodies. I will suggest using the **Yab-Yum** position from our *Breathe With Me* Practice earlier, but if you find a position that works better for you, then by all means use your own. Set a timer for five to ten minutes, whatever feels doable for your first couple of times trying this.

Next, relax all of your facial muscles. A tense body and face make tense lips, and we need full relaxation of the body to welcome our partners to kiss us deeply.

You can try some different facial relaxation exercises like taking deep breaths or fluttering the lips. Sometimes a facial massage is helpful.

Next, decide who's leading and who will follow. Lean in close, and whoever is the leader, kiss your partner's upper lip with both of your lips. Let your lips fall open and juicy, and suck on their upper lip gently.

Then do the same with your partner's lower lip. Kiss their lower lip with your entire being, suck on it, maybe nibble on it a little, and focus completely on this small part of their body.

Next, kiss both of your partner's lips together with your whole mouth, slowly, fully. Linger for a while, feel both of their lips connected with yours. Notice the energy building and continue repeating this practice for the duration of the time set.

Do their lips quiver? Are they kissing you back? How does one lip feel different from the other? Do you want to involve your tongue? You can try different angles, different ways of breathing, different parts of the inside of their mouth - you can get more and more explorative as you go.

When the time is up, switch roles.

RECORD & REFLECT

Here is your space to reflect on this practice as a couple.
Take some time, be honest, and answer truthfully.

What was the main takeaway/lesson from this practice?

_____

_____

_____

_____

What did you like about this practice?

_____

_____

_____

_____

What was most challenging about this practice?

_____

_____

_____

_____

RATE THIS PRACTICE:

BORING/UNPLEASANT				FINE/HELPFUL			INSPIRING/SUPER FUN		
1	2	3	4	5	6	7	8	9	10

27
SLOWER THAN YOU'D LIKE TO

We often want to jump into sexy time quickly and all at once when we get excited. This practice is about slowing down, feeling each step of the way, and sitting with your desire.

THE PRACTICE

With this one, you can get right into all the good stuff you like to do without delay, but the challenge is to slow everything down. If you're starting with kissing, then make it last a little longer than normal.

Prolong the kissing period, slowly removing one bit of clothing at a time rather than stripping in a frenzy. If your hands start to wander, move slowly, and caress other parts of the body before going straight to the genitals. How does it feel to linger on the shoulders a little longer?

What sensations arise when your partner squeezes your breasts for a prolonged period before getting down between your legs? How does it feel to be teased around your vulva, or your penis, before they actually touch you where you really want them to?

Make every step of the way its own whole chapter in the story, and then see if you can enter just as slowly, with just as much anticipation.

Let the tension build, let the desire build, and let the juices course heavy and hot through your body before you give in.

RECORD & REFLECT

Here is your space to reflect on this practice as a couple.
Take some time, be honest, and answer truthfully.

What was the main takeaway/lesson from this practice?

_____

_____

_____

_____

What did you like about this practice?

_____

_____

_____

_____

What was most challenging about this practice?

_____

_____

_____

_____

RATE THIS PRACTICE:

BORING/UNPLEASANT				FINE/HELPFUL			INSPIRING/SUPER FUN		
1	2	3	4	5	6	7	8	9	10

28
LET'S GET WET

Isn't that what foreplay is all about?

Now we're getting in the shower. We're getting wet!

THE PRACTICE

Step into the shower together and have the act of cleaning one another's bodies be your foreplay. One person at a time will get scrubbed down, so have one person be in action while the other receives, but of course, you can go back and forth.

Lather some soap in your hands and rub down every inch of your partner's body, from top to bottom. Wash their hair, slowly, massaging their scalp as you go, and let them rinse their hair in the hot water while you play with their nipples or continue to lather other parts of their body.

Maybe you start to fondle them a little as they rinse, putting a finger inside them or gently stroking their cock. Take your time lathering and scrubbing and rubbing, it is a true luxury to be bathed by someone else and can make for deep relaxation and heightened sensation in the body.

Then, switch roles, if you haven't already done so along the way until you've both had the experience of being thoroughly washed and bathed by your partner.

Once you've both been thoroughly cleansed, use the wall of the shower as a back rest and kiss passionately under the hot water, and see where things go from here.

RECORD & REFLECT

Here is your space to reflect on this practice as a couple.
Take some time, be honest, and answer truthfully.

What was the main takeaway/lesson from this practice?

_____

_____

_____

_____

What did you like about this practice?

_____

_____

_____

_____

What was most challenging about this practice?

_____

_____

_____

_____

RATE THIS PRACTICE:

BORING/UNPLEASANT				FINE/HELPFUL			INSPIRING/SUPER FUN		
1	2	3	4	5	6	7	8	9	10

29
TEASING/EDGING

How does it feel to withhold the climax from your sex? How does it feel to get right to the brink of the big O, and then to withhold that sensation, to prolong that release? How long can you stand to tease one another before it's too much? How much bigger can your orgasm get if you don't get to have it right away?

Teasing and edging are ways of creating anticipation so that when the orgasm can finally happen, it feels all that much more incredible. This is also commonly used in kink, wherein the sub must beg their dom to let them cum, but we'll get into how to incorporate teasing and edging in kink and BDSM later in our journey. For now, we're focused on foreplay.

THE PRACTICE

Sexy time has commenced, and we're playing around with our hands and maybe our mouths. The challenge is to get your partner to the brink of their orgasm, without letting them have it.

Try to use just your hands to bring them to this point, then, when you can feel their body start to tense, when they tell you they're about to cum, stop what you're doing.

For people with vulvas, a good way to stop without creating pain or losing momentum is to cup your hand over their vulva and pubic mound (the entirety of the space from the bottom of the vulva up past the top of the labia and clitoris, over the mons pubis (the area where pubic hair grows)) and apply some gentle pressure in holding them by this part of their body while you let them come down from the brink of their orgasm.

For people with penises, it can feel supportive to gently cup the balls, or apply gentle pressure with the palm to the low belly (the space between the penis and the belly button).

Once they've come away from their orgasm, you can start up again, maybe this time using your mouth.

Repeat this practice a couple of times, until you think your partner has withstood enough torture, and then you can finish them off however you'd like, or however they'd like.

By this point, you can ask them what they want, and how they want to cum, and you can give that to them. But let that tension build and let that teasing be the main focus of the experience.

RECORD & REFLECT

Here is your space to reflect on this practice as a couple.
Take some time, be honest, and answer truthfully.

What was the main takeaway/lesson from this practice?

_____

_____

_____

_____

What did you like about this practice?

_____

_____

_____

_____

What was most challenging about this practice?

_____

_____

_____

_____

RATE THIS PRACTICE:

BORING/UNPLEASANT				FINE/HELPFUL			INSPIRING/SUPER FUN		
1	2	3	4	5	6	7	8	9	10

30
STRIP-TEASE

It's pretty straightforward: Everyone likes a good strip-tease.

However, just like with dirty talk, many of us find it challenging to take ourselves seriously when trying to perform something of this nature.

My suggestion is to try a strip-tease for yourself in the mirror first. Recognize your own sensuality and get comfy stripping for yourself before you invite your partner. Get all the giggles out beforehand!

However, you'll almost certainly get the giggles when trying this with your partner as well, and that's okay! Again, sex isn't supposed to be serious all the time. Let yourselves laugh, laugh together, but then really try to get into the headspace of the stripper for your boo.

See if you can get outside of your head and make this a real, proper strip-tease.

THE PRACTICE

Decide who is going to be the stripper and who will be the receiver.

The stripper will begin fully clothed but should put on something underneath their clothes that they feel confident and sexy in, that they're excited for their partner to see them in.

Sit your partner (the receiver) down somewhere they can watch you, perhaps on a chair or couch, and put on some music that makes you feel sensual and gets you in the zone.

Fully clothed to start, play with teasing them one garment at a time, tugging at the waist of your pants or playing with the collar of your shirt, making eye contact with them all the while.

Then, very slowly, maybe one button at a time, start to remove one article of clothing at a time to reveal whatever undergarments you're wearing under all the layers. Let them see you in this get-up for a while, let them soak you up and take you in in all of your seductive glory.

After a while of showing off your sexy look, then you can start removing pieces, once again keeping eye contact with them the entire time, very slowly, bit by bit.

Interact with them a little if that feels fun. Ask them to tug on the toes of your tights (if you're wearing them) or unzip the back of you, or however else they can be involved in little exciting ways.

Take as long as you want so your partner can really drink you in, and strip down as much or as little as you'd like.

When you're finished removing garments, you can slink over and sit on their lap. See where things go from here!

RECORD & REFLECT

Here is your space to reflect on this practice as a couple.
Take some time, be honest, and answer truthfully.

What was the main takeaway/lesson from this practice?

_____

_____

_____

_____

What did you like about this practice?

_____

_____

_____

_____

What was most challenging about this practice?

_____

_____

_____

_____

RATE THIS PRACTICE:

BORING/UNPLEASANT				FINE/HELPFUL			INSPIRING/SUPER FUN		
1	2	3	4	5	6	7	8	9	10

31
SPONTANEITY

Sometimes, there's nothing sexier than a little spontaneity, a little being caught off guard, a sexy little surprise.

THE PRACTICE

This one can be very open-ended but operates on one uniting premise: Be spontaneous! Get them when they least expect it.

Sometimes the best way to spice things up in the bedroom is to spice things up outside of the bedroom, to add excitement to those little mundane moments in everyday life when you're both just going about your day without sex on the brain. Put sex on their brain!

Some ideas: Maybe you're just driving along, listening to music, and all of a sudden you lean over and start nibbling on their ear. Maybe you slide a hand down between their legs while they're steering (or trying to steer).

Maybe you're out for dinner and you slide your foot between their calves, or perhaps you run a hand up and down their inner thigh under the table.

Maybe they're making dinner and their ass is just looking smack-able, so you come up behind them, grab them by the hair and bend them over the counter.

Whatever it may be, see if you can make a game out of it. Who can catch the other off guard? Who can surprise the other the most? Who can be the most discreet in public? Once you start to play around with this little game, it will become harder and harder to surprise one another, so things can get quite creative and interesting.

RECORD & REFLECT

Here is your space to reflect on this practice as a couple.
Take some time, be honest, and answer truthfully.

What was the main takeaway/lesson from this practice?

_____

_____

_____

_____

What did you like about this practice?

_____

_____

_____

_____

What was most challenging about this practice?

_____

_____

_____

_____

RATE THIS PRACTICE:

BORING/UNPLEASANT				FINE/HELPFUL			INSPIRING/SUPER FUN		
1	2	3	4	5	6	7	8	9	10

32
EROTIC MASSAGE

This is a very traditional form of foreplay, and it is seen across many different sexuality philosophies and modalities. It is tried and true and so widely used because everyone loves a good old-fashioned massage.

But how can we go one step further? How can we take massage to the realm of the erotic?

THE PRACTICE

Choose a giver and a receiver. Lay the receiver down on their tummy on a comfortable surface, most ideally a bed.

Select some form of massage oil (any form of oil can work, natural oils such as coconut oil or almond oil are best for most bodies and can be mixed with other essential oils for scent/relaxation) and use it generously.

Decide either to start at the top of your partner's body (neck/shoulders) or the bottom (feet) and slowly start to massage every inch of their body from your starting point upward or downward.

Now and then, give their ass a little spank or give some part of their body a little nibble. As you massage, you can see about incorporating different sensations, such as feathers or pinwheels to stimulate different sensations.

After you've worked your way over their entire body, flip them over so they're now laying on their back, and do the same on this side.

This time, you can let them watch you, or you can choose to blindfold them to encourage deeper feelings. On both sides of the body, do not skip over the genitals if they're accessible. Involve them just as any other part of the body. Make sure every part of the body gets equal attention as you explore different methods of massaging your lover. Let them fully relax into the pleasure you are serving.

EXTRA NAUGHTY MASSAGE

Place a vibrator either on their genitals or inside of them and leave it there for the entirety of the massage. Don't keep moving it around or stimulating them with it, just turn it on and leave it pressed against their clit (or around the scrotum/balls or the perineum on a man), or inside of them, and watch how this changes things and drives them wild.

If they cum, let them cum - we're not teasing this time. Let them orgasm and then continue with your massage without removing the vibrator from their body.

RECORD & REFLECT

Here is your space to reflect on this practice as a couple.
Take some time, be honest, and answer truthfully.

What was the main takeaway/lesson from this practice?

_____

_____

_____

_____

What did you like about this practice?

_____

_____

_____

_____

What was most challenging about this practice?

_____

_____

_____

_____

RATE THIS PRACTICE:

BORING/UNPLEASANT				FINE/HELPFUL			INSPIRING/SUPER FUN		
1	2	3	4	5	6	7	8	9	10

33
ONLY MY HANDS

Some good standard hand stuff is always welcome in foreplay and in general sex itself. There is so much pleasure that can be accessed by just using our hands on our partner's bodies.

The goal is to get your partner off by using just your hands. Many people claim they simply cannot cum just from hand stuff, and for some, this may very well be true, but for many, they've simply never had the patience to let their partner try to get them off with their hands. We may get worried it'll take too long, or our partner will get fed up with us, so we give up and get to the other stuff that we know does the trick quickly. Try to avoid this need for speed, and let your partner explore different ways to pleasure you with their hands - even if it takes all night!

THE PRACTICE

Lay your partner down somewhere comfortable, ideally a bed, and have them close their eyes and relax their body completely.

Spread their legs a little and start to caress their inner thighs with your fingertips. Explore touching them around the upper inner thighs for a while, running your hands up and down their belly, up and down their legs, and use some form of lubrication so everything feels really nice and smooth and easy to move around.

Slowly gravitate toward their genitals.

FOR PEOPLE WITH VULVAS:

Start by gently tickling around their labia, running your fingers up and down the sides around their vaginal opening. Try to avoid going straight for the clitoris, see if you can stimulate the other parts of the body first.

Activate as much of them as possible, and then play with clitoral stimulation. Once they feel more and more aroused in your hands, you can play with penetration if that is something your partner likes. Try inserting one finger at a time into their vagina, while continuing to move your fingers in small circles around their clitoris and running your fingers up and down the outsides of their vaginal opening. Continue from here in the ways you know your partner gets the most pleasure until they cum. Don't give up just because this way may take a little longer than the others.

FOR PEOPLE WITH PENISES:

Start with gently caressing their balls and perineum and play with these parts of them for a moment before engaging the penis. If the penis is still soft, gently run the palm of your hand up from the balls toward the penis and apply slight pressure to tug on the penis a little bit without grabbing hold of it.

If your partner enjoys it, you can gently tickle the tip of the penis for more stimulation, this is very sensitive on most bodies. Play around and explore to see what arouses your partner. If/when the penis becomes hard, start stroking by gently wrapping your hand around the shaft and moving your hand up and down. You can continue to fondle their balls while you stroke. From here continue in the ways your partner responds to and explore different techniques. Be patient.

RECORD & REFLECT

Here is your space to reflect on this practice as a couple.
Take some time, be honest, and answer truthfully.

What was the main takeaway/lesson from this practice?

_____

_____

_____

_____

What did you like about this practice?

_____

_____

_____

_____

What was most challenging about this practice?

_____

_____

_____

_____

RATE THIS PRACTICE:

BORING/UNPLEASANT				FINE/HELPFUL			INSPIRING/SUPER FUN		
1	2	3	4	5	6	7	8	9	10

34
ONLY MY MOUTH

Very similar to *Only My Hands*, but this time we don't get to use our hands, this time is only about the mouth.

The goal is to get your partner off using just your mouth. Many people claim they simply cannot cum just from oral sex, and for some, this may very well be true, but for many, they've simply never had the patience to let their partner try to get them off this way.

We may get worried it'll take too long, or our partner will get fed up with us, so we give up and get to the other stuff that we know does the trick quickly. Try to avoid this need for speed, and let your partner explore different ways to pleasure you with their mouth if it takes all night!

THE PRACTICE

Lay your partner down somewhere comfortable, ideally a bed, and have them close their eyes and relax their body completely. Spread their legs a little and start to kiss them or run your tongue up and down their inner thighs.

Explore licking them around the upper inner thighs for a while, running your tongue up and down their belly, up and down their legs, use lots of saliva or edible lubrication (coconut oil or other edible oil) so everything feels nice and smooth and easy to move around.

Slowly gravitate toward their genitals.

FOR PEOPLE WITH VULVAS:

Start by gently tickling around their labia, running your tongue up and down the sides around their vaginal opening. Try to avoid going straight for the clitoris, see if you can stimulate the other parts of the body first.

Activate as much of them as possible with kissing, sucking, licking, biting, and then play with clitoral stimulation. Once they feel more and more aroused in your mouth, you can play with penetration with the tongue if that is something your partner likes. Continue from here in the ways you know your partner gets the most pleasure until they cum.

Don't give up just because this way may take a little longer than the others.

FOR PEOPLE WITH PENISES:

Start with gently sucking on their balls and ticking their perineum with your tongue. Play with these parts of them for a moment before engaging the penis. If the penis is still soft, gently run the tongue up from the balls toward the penis and gently wrap your lips around the penis tip, applying slight pressure to tug on the penis a little bit without grabbing hold of it. If your partner enjoys it, you can gently tickle the tip of the penis with your tongue for more stimulation, this is very sensitive on most bodies.

Play around and explore to see what arouses your partner. If/when the penis becomes hard, start stroking by gently wrapping your lips around the shaft and moving your mouth up and down. You can continue to fondle their balls in between sucking and stroking. From here continue in the ways your partner responds to and explore different techniques. Be patient.

RECORD & REFLECT

Here is your space to reflect on this practice as a couple.
Take some time, be honest, and answer truthfully.

What was the main takeaway/lesson from this practice?

_____

_____

_____

_____

What did you like about this practice?

_____

_____

_____

_____

What was most challenging about this practice?

_____

_____

_____

_____

RATE THIS PRACTICE:

BORING/UNPLEASANT				FINE/HELPFUL			INSPIRING/SUPER FUN		
1	2	3	4	5	6	7	8	9	10

35
TOYS ONLY

This time it's all about the toys. Sometimes partners have a hard time introducing toys because they feel that using a toy means they aren't good enough to pleasure their partner on their own. Think of sex toys as your ally rather than your competition.

They are there to support you on your partnered pleasure journey; they are there to enhance things for both of you. And let's be real, no matter how wicked your hands are, they can't vibrate, and they can't reach the places some toys can, and that's okay!

THE PRACTICE

Lay your partner down somewhere comfortable, ideally a bed, and have them close their eyes and relax their body completely. Spread their legs a little and start to run whatever toy you may be using up and down their inner thighs.

If using something that vibrates, explore the upper inner thighs for a while, running the toy up and down their belly, up and down their legs, using lots of lubrication (coconut oil or other natural oil) so everything feels nice and smooth and easy to move around.

Slowly gravitate toward their genitals.

As always start slowly with whatever you're using and build from there. The goal, remember, is to use only the toys, so refrain from using your hands, your mouth, or any part of your body. Unless you're holding the toy in place for them, your hands should not be touching them. They should be exclusively engaged with the toy you've selected.

RECORD & REFLECT

Here is your space to reflect on this practice as a couple.
Take some time, be honest, and answer truthfully.

What was the main takeaway/lesson from this practice?

_____

_____

_____

_____

What did you like about this practice?

_____

_____

_____

_____

What was most challenging about this practice?

_____

_____

_____

_____

RATE THIS PRACTICE:

BORING/UNPLEASANT				FINE/HELPFUL			INSPIRING/SUPER FUN		
1	2	3	4	5	6	7	8	9	10

36
ABOVE THE BELT

Most often when we think of foreplay, we think immediately of the genitals. Can we challenge ourselves to turn our partner on without going below the belt?

There are so many erogenous zones throughout the upper body, however, they often get forgotten about in favor of the more direct, immediate approach to things by heading down under.

By refraining from this temptation, we can see what pleasure lives in the rest of the body—the head and neck, the ears, the shoulders, the breasts, the nipples, the belly, the back, and the hands and fingers. There is so much to explore!

THE PRACTICE

Have your partner seated, and sit behind them, wrapping your legs around their waist or straddling out to the sides of their body.

Start at their hips, placing your hands on their hips and squeezing with as much pressure as they like, continuously upward from their hips up the sides of their body.

Tell them to let you know when a particular spot feels really good and spend a little extra time there. Once you reach their armpits, squeeze down one arm at a time with both hands on the same arm.

Squeeze the palms of their hands with your hands, a little hand massage, and then tug on their fingers a little bit. Do the same with both arms, and then start to squeeze across their shoulders and up their neck.

Next, move down their chest. If they have breasts, squeeze them and, regardless, give their nipples a pinch, stimulating their entire upper body with your hands.

Wherever they ask you to linger, or you notice a physical reaction from them, stay there a little longer and pay more attention to these places. Once you've squeezed all over their upper body, ask them where they'd like you to hold your hands.

Perhaps they'll say over their chest or their lower belly, maybe over their shoulders. Wherever they mention, place both hands in that place, apply a bit of pressure and hold them there.

RECORD & REFLECT

Here is your space to reflect on this practice as a couple.
Take some time, be honest, and answer truthfully.

What was the main takeaway/lesson from this practice?

_____

_____

_____

_____

What did you like about this practice?

_____

_____

_____

_____

What was most challenging about this practice?

_____

_____

_____

_____

RATE THIS PRACTICE:

BORING/UNPLEASANT				FINE/HELPFUL			INSPIRING/SUPER FUN		
1	2	3	4	5	6	7	8	9	10

37
THE OTHER PARTS OF ME

This is very similar to *Above The Belt* in premise, working with the fact that there are so many erogenous zones on the body apart from the genitals.

The goal is to explore sensations outside of the genitals. Can we challenge ourselves to turn our partners on without touching their genitals?

There are so many erogenous zones throughout the body, however, they often get forgotten about in favor of the more direct, immediate approach to things by heading down under.

By refraining from this temptation, however, we can see what pleasure lives in the rest of the body - the head and neck, the breasts, the nipples, the belly, the legs, and the feet. There is so much to explore!

THE PRACTICE

Have your partner standing, perhaps holding onto the back of a chair or near a wall for stability/support and stand behind them.

Start at their feet, placing your hands over the tops of their feet and toes and squeezing their feet with as much pressure as they like. Continue upward from here, one leg at a time, up their calves and thighs to their hips.

Once you've explored both legs, grab hold of their hips and continue onward through the same practice as *Above The Belt* with them remaining standing.

Tell them to let you know when a particular spot feels really good and spend a little extra time there. Once you reach their armpits, squeeze down one arm at a time with both hands on the same arm. Squeeze the palms of their hands with your hands, a little hand massage, and then tug on their fingers a little bit. Do the same with both arms, and then start to squeeze across their shoulders and up their neck.

Next, move down their chest. If they have breasts, squeeze their breasts and, regardless, give their nipples a pinch, stimulating their entire upper body with your hands.

Wherever they ask you to linger, or you notice a physical reaction from them, stay there a little longer and pay more attention to these places. Once you've squeezed all over their body, ask them where they'd like you to hold your hands.

Perhaps they'll say over their chest or their lower belly, maybe over their pelvis or genitals. Wherever they mention, place both hands in that place, apply a bit of pressure and hold them there.

Breathe together in silence for a few moments.

RECORD & REFLECT

Here is your space to reflect on this practice as a couple.
Take some time, be honest, and answer truthfully.

What was the main takeaway/lesson from this practice?

_____

_____

_____

_____

What did you like about this practice?

_____

_____

_____

_____

What was most challenging about this practice?

_____

_____

_____

_____

RATE THIS PRACTICE:

BORING/UNPLEASANT				FINE/HELPFUL			INSPIRING/SUPER FUN		
1	2	3	4	5	6	7	8	9	10

CHAPTER 6.

FANTASIES

INTRODUCTION TO FANTASIES

We all have fantasies, whether we like to admit it or not. Often, we feel a lot of shame about our fantasies because we've been told that to experience particular sexual fantasies is dirty, wrong, perverted, too freaky, too weird, offensive to our partners, or a smorgasbord of other adjectives that cause us to keep our fantasies to ourselves.

In reality, all fantasies are normal, no matter how bizarre or mundane. Most of the time, our fantasies are caused by our lived experience in one way or another, and in this way, they are a re-claiming of our reality through our sexuality.

The psychology behind fantasies is a whole other book, but for the sake of our journey together, I will just leave you with the very truthful affirmation that your fantasies are normal and that there is nothing wrong with you for having them.

With this in mind, move through this chapter of practices with an open mind to both your own and your partner's fantasies.

Feel the assurance that while both of you will most likely have very different fantasies and will most likely be very surprised by one another's fantasies when you start opening up about them, there is always space for all fantasies to be expressed in one way or another - of course, within the boundaries of consent and morality.

Be playful with these practices, be very open-minded, and let your partner into your unique, inner world.

38
SETTING THE STAGE

This one is more about your physical space, your bedroom. Being able to live your sexual fantasies must start with being in your fantasy space.

THE PRACTICE

Sit down, close your eyes, and take a few moments to envision the most sensual bedroom you could imagine, a bedroom that you'd never want to leave. That you'd wake up feeling horny and full of bliss every morning, a sexual sanctuary for you and your lover to spend hours exploring one another.

Get all the details, the colors of the walls, the floors, bedspread and sheets, things on the walls, everything that makes this room your sexual fantasy space.

Now, open your eyes, and look around your actual bedroom. How do the two align? Is your dream room very similar to your existing bedroom, or is it very different?

How then, regardless of how close or how different these two spaces are, could you bring your existing space closer to the sexy bedroom of your dreams, within your means? Could you start by simply moving some things around? Could you paint the walls or get rid of those flannel sheets you've had for 15 years? Can you bring in a plant or some flowers? Do you want to add some kink gear to the space?

Now, make some changes! Of course, you don't have to go all out and build a sex dungeon at the drop of a hat (unless you want to). Rather, see how you can incorporate some of your fantasy into your reality in your physical space. You may be surprised how the smallest little tweaks can change the energy drastically!

RECORD & REFLECT

Here is your space to reflect on this practice as a couple.
Take some time, be honest, and answer truthfully.

What was the main takeaway/lesson from this practice?

_____

_____

_____

_____

What did you like about this practice?

_____

_____

_____

_____

What was most challenging about this practice?

_____

_____

_____

_____

RATE THIS PRACTICE:

BORING/UNPLEASANT				FINE/HELPFUL			INSPIRING/SUPER FUN		
1	2	3	4	5	6	7	8	9	10

39

SEXY PLAYLIST

Many of us have dabbled in the art of creating sexy playlists here and there over the years, but have you ever tried making a collaborative sexy playlist?

THE PRACTICE

Sit down with your partner and brainstorm the songs that make you both feel like a sexual god/goddess. Those songs that just do it for you, that just get you both going.

Make a playlist of all of these songs, alternating your selections so that both partners' songs are equally in the mix.

Then, put the playlist on, live your sensual fantasy, and get freaky!

RECORD & REFLECT

Here is your space to reflect on this practice as a couple.
Take some time, be honest, and answer truthfully.

What was the main takeaway/lesson from this practice?

_____

_____

_____

_____

What did you like about this practice?

_____

_____

_____

_____

What was most challenging about this practice?

_____

_____

_____

_____

RATE THIS PRACTICE:

BORING/UNPLEASANT				FINE/HELPFUL			INSPIRING/SUPER FUN		
1	2	3	4	5	6	7	8	9	10

40
DIRTY LITTLE SECRETS

This is the time to get vulnerable, to get real, to crack open your sexual vault, and let your partner see you fully, in all of your dirty, weird, wild quirks and secrets. We all have secret sexual fantasies that we've never shared or lived out, and it might actually scare us to admit to them or explore them, to recognize them as equally part of us as all of our other quirks and desires.

It is important to move forward with safety and recognition of both your and your partner's boundaries, but it can also be quite interesting to share your dirty little secrets. You never know, maybe you and your partner have something in common.

THE PRACTICE

Sit facing back-to-back, so you're resting your weight against your partner's back. Without looking at each other, both partners will share one or two fantasies of theirs that they've never had the opportunity to live out or share with anyone.

Don't interrupt your partner while they're sharing. Instead, absorb what they say, really think about it, consider it, and feel out if it's something you'd be interested in trying or not.

Once both people have spoken, and you feel ready, turn around to face one another, and have a chat about each fantasy. Ask questions. What it is about the fantasy specifically that turns them on? How do they imagine it playing out? How long have they had it?

Then, discuss if their fantasy is something you'd be interested in trying. If you're not comfortable with the exact thing they've described, how could you modify it so that you would be more comfortable exploring their desires with them?

RECORD & REFLECT

Here is your space to reflect on this practice as a couple.
Take some time, be honest, and answer truthfully.

What was the main takeaway/lesson from this practice?

_____

_____

_____

_____

What did you like about this practice?

_____

_____

_____

_____

What was most challenging about this practice?

_____

_____

_____

_____

RATE THIS PRACTICE:

BORING/UNPLEASANT				FINE/HELPFUL			INSPIRING/SUPER FUN		
1	2	3	4	5	6	7	8	9	10

41
FANTASY CARDS

This is where all the fantasies, big and small, can come into play! Go into this one with an open mind; you never know what you're going to get when you throw sexy activities into a hat. You may surprise yourself!

THE PRACTICE

Separately, each writes five to ten fantasies you have on individual pieces of paper. Fold up the fantasies and throw them all into a hat together, mixing them up thoroughly.

Place this hat in your bedroom somewhere, and whenever you feel like you want to mix things up in the bedroom, pull a Fantasy Card from the hat to explore that evening.

They don't all have to happen at once; these can be explored over time, whenever you're feeling in the mood.

RECORD & REFLECT

Here is your space to reflect on this practice as a couple.
Take some time, be honest, and answer truthfully.

What was the main takeaway/lesson from this practice?

_____

_____

_____

_____

What did you like about this practice?

_____

_____

_____

_____

What was most challenging about this practice?

_____

_____

_____

_____

RATE THIS PRACTICE:

BORING/UNPLEASANT				FINE/HELPFUL			INSPIRING/SUPER FUN		
1	2	3	4	5	6	7	8	9	10

42

SEXY CHARADES

Ready to test your acting skills? Ready to turn an innocent family game naughty? Sexy charades are a great way to express your fantasies without having to verbally express them, which can feel easier and lighter than baring your darkest secrets in very serious talking form.

THE PRACTICE

As there will only be two of you, you will be coming up with your own scenarios to act out, for your partner to guess.

Take turns acting and guessing. The goal is to act out a fantasy of yours, without using words, until your partner guesses what you're trying to act out. Just like regular charades but make it naughty!

Once they guess your fantasy, switch roles. And keep tabs on the things your partner acts out.

RECORD & REFLECT

Here is your space to reflect on this practice as a couple.
Take some time, be honest, and answer truthfully.

What was the main takeaway/lesson from this practice?

_____

_____

_____

_____

What did you like about this practice?

_____

_____

_____

_____

What was most challenging about this practice?

_____

_____

_____

_____

RATE THIS PRACTICE:

BORING/UNPLEASANT				FINE/HELPFUL			INSPIRING/SUPER FUN		
1	2	3	4	5	6	7	8	9	10

43
FINISH MY SENTENCE

How well do you know your partner's sexuality? This practice operates on the premise that we typically think we know exactly what our partner wants, however, we are very often at least a little bit off track, simply based on a lack of communication or an assumption here or there.

The saying "we finish each other's sentences" is most often used to express how close two people are or how similar a pair may be, so what happens when we apply this to our unspoken sexual fantasies?

THE PRACTICE

This is mostly a word game, but I'll encourage you to see how you can live them out once the scenario has been built between the two of you.

Start a timer for 30 seconds, and choose which person is starting. When the timer starts, the first person will begin to describe one of their fantasy scenarios and continue to elaborate on this scenario until the timer goes off.

The second partner will then start the timer and pick up describing the fantasy where the first person left off. They will follow along the same train of thought as their partner, to see if they can guess where their partner was going with things. They'll stop speaking when the timer is up, and the first person will again start speaking, picking up where their partner left off.

As one partner builds upon what is said by the other, back and forth, a mutual fantasy will be built. You can keep going back and forth as much as you'd like until you feel you've created a complete scenario and sexual encounter.

RECORD & REFLECT

Here is your space to reflect on this practice as a couple.
Take some time, be honest, and answer truthfully.

What was the main takeaway/lesson from this practice?

_____

_____

_____

_____

What did you like about this practice?

_____

_____

_____

_____

What was most challenging about this practice?

_____

_____

_____

_____

RATE THIS PRACTICE:

BORING/UNPLEASANT		FINE/HELPFUL		INSPIRING/SUPER FUN	
1 2 3	4	5 6	7	8 9	10

44
FANTASY
SCENES/SCENARIOS

Let's look to Hollywood for this one. What are those scenes from the movies that just get you going? Who is that actor/actress you've always dreamed of being on that beach or in that shower with? It is quite common actually, for us to build our sex life up around what we've seen in the movies, as typically, we don't have many other frames of reference as adolescents growing up in a world that doesn't offer much by way of sexual education.

This causes movies and TV to play major roles in our sexual development, which has them trickling into our fantasies.

THE PRACTICE

Decide on a movie scene/scenario that lives in your fantasies rent-free. See if you can find that movie or just the scene, so you and your partner can watch it together.

Watch the scene play out together, pay attention to the details, and express to your partner what specifically it is about this particular scene that does it for you.

Then, do your best to recreate the scene! See if you can really get into it. Go as far as moving things around, dressing up, or drinking the drinks they're drinking or eating the food on screen. You can get really silly and theatrical.

Play out the scene and see where it takes you! Maybe you become those characters, or maybe you take a spin on things in a different direction. If it's not actually a sex scene that you're acting out, how can you make it sexier? How could those characters get down and dirty in their situation, in that lunch restaurant, in that courtroom? The possibilities are endless!

RECORD & REFLECT

Here is your space to reflect on this practice as a couple.
Take some time, be honest, and answer truthfully.

What was the main takeaway/lesson from this practice?

_____

_____

_____

_____

What did you like about this practice?

_____

_____

_____

_____

What was most challenging about this practice?

_____

_____

_____

_____

RATE THIS PRACTICE:

BORING/UNPLEASANT				FINE/HELPFUL			INSPIRING/SUPER FUN		
1	2	3	4	5	6	7	8	9	10

45
EROTIC DANCE

Have you ever watched an erotic dancer, a stripper, a burlesque performer, a music video, or even someone in a club and fantasized about dirty dancing like the sluttiest version of yourself?

Have you ever wished you could watch your partner get dirty and roll around like the strippers in the club?

The first step to living erotic dance fantasies is to release any conception of **slut shaming** you may hold - from your upbringing or background or wherever it comes from - and recognize that we all have a little slut inside of us that wants to be let out to play.

THE PRACTICE

THE DANCER:

If you've always dreamed of being the one doing the dancing, now's your chance to live that fantasy. Wear something that makes you feel you are at your most sexy and confident, and clear some space so you can dance.

Get inspired by watching whatever it was that inspired you to want to move this way (maybe you need to watch a couple of Britney music videos or go to the strip club), and then pick some music to dance to (maybe use the same music that inspired you).

Invite your partner into the space, sit them down, and let out your absolute sluttiest self to roll around on the floor for them, give them a sexy lap dance, tease them, and let them watch you strut your sexual power.

THE FANTASIZER:

If you've been dreaming of the day your partner took the stage and danced for you so you can sit back and watch them, you may be surprised what your boo is willing to do to satisfy your desires.

Show them, or tell them, how you want them to dance for you, in as much or as little detail as you feel the need to share.

Perhaps go out and buy something for them to wear for you. Encourage them to give you a little show. It could even help to throw dollar bills at them for dramatic effect or to set the stage for them to come out onto.

Make them feel confident and comfortable, and then really soak it up.

RECORD & REFLECT

Here is your space to reflect on this practice as a couple.
Take some time, be honest, and answer truthfully.

What was the main takeaway/lesson from this practice?

_____

_____

_____

_____

What did you like about this practice?

_____

_____

_____

_____

What was most challenging about this practice?

_____

_____

_____

_____

RATE THIS PRACTICE:

BORING/UNPLEASANT				FINE/HELPFUL			INSPIRING/SUPER FUN		
1	2	3	4	5	6	7	8	9	10

46
"WHO AM I?"

This one is quite similar to charades, using impressions and acting to indulge fantasies, but this time you can use your voice and go beyond the game toward the world of role-playing.

THE PRACTICE

Take an opportunity when your partner is either busy or not home (if you live together) and decide on a fantasy either you have, or you know is one of your partner's fantasies. Get yourself into the character of that fantasy (maybe it's a professor they had, or Elvis, or Wonder Woman). Be ready for when they get home or approach them in character if they're already home.

The goal is for you to approach them in character, and they'll go along with it until they're able to guess who you're supposed to be, or what the scenario is that's happening. Once they guess, they'll be able to get into it with you, so you can play it out together!

RECORD & REFLECT

Here is your space to reflect on this practice as a couple.
Take some time, be honest, and answer truthfully.

What was the main takeaway/lesson from this practice?

_____

_____

_____

_____

What did you like about this practice?

_____

_____

_____

_____

What was most challenging about this practice?

_____

_____

_____

_____

RATE THIS PRACTICE:

BORING/UNPLEASANT				FINE/HELPFUL			INSPIRING/SUPER FUN		
1	2	3	4	5	6	7	8	9	10

47
YOU ARE...

This one is quite similar to charades and *"Who Am I?"*, using impressions and acting to indulge fantasies, but this time you can add a bit of domination while using your voice and going beyond the game toward the world of role-playing.

THE PRACTICE

This is very similar to the last practice, except this time you decide who your partner is playing, without telling them.

You can try to make this one as spontaneous as the last, but it may be easiest to establish that you're within the parameters of a game prior to beginning, so it's less off-pulling for your partner when you start treating them quite differently.

You will choose a role from one of your or your partner's fantasies and assign it to your partner, and then begin regarding your partner as though they were that person from your fantasy until they guess who they're supposed to be.

FOR EXAMPLE:

You have decided your partner is that sexy professor you had back in university. You walk over to where they're sitting on the couch, and sit on the armrest, crossing one leg over the other and leaning close.

You start praising their mind, complimenting their intellect, asking if they can give you some more one-on-one style classes and if they can take you to their office. And so on, until they catch on, and begin to play along.

RECORD & REFLECT

Here is your space to reflect on this practice as a couple.
Take some time, be honest, and answer truthfully.

What was the main takeaway/lesson from this practice?

_____

_____

_____

_____

What did you like about this practice?

_____

_____

_____

_____

What was most challenging about this practice?

_____

_____

_____

_____

RATE THIS PRACTICE:

BORING/UNPLEASANT				FINE/HELPFUL			INSPIRING/SUPER FUN		
1	2	3	4	5	6	7	8	9	10

48
DRESS ME UP

Sometimes our fantasies aren't all that elaborate.

Sometimes it's as simple as really wanting to see your partner wear a certain thing, or not wear a certain thing, and with consent, this can be quite easy to achieve.

THE PRACTICE

The name of the game is to dress up! Choose who will be the dresser and who the dressee, and let the dresser have full creative freedom.

You can choose to go shopping together, or you can choose to surprise your partner with what they're going to be wearing. Go all out though - get the whole costume of your dreams for your partner to seduce you in (this can be anything from crotch-less panties to coveralls).

Then, let them come out in their new look and sink into their new role. Let them give you your fantasy.

RECORD & REFLECT

Here is your space to reflect on this practice as a couple.
Take some time, be honest, and answer truthfully.

What was the main takeaway/lesson from this practice?

_____

_____

_____

_____

What did you like about this practice?

_____

_____

_____

_____

What was most challenging about this practice?

_____

_____

_____

_____

RATE THIS PRACTICE:

BORING/UNPLEASANT				FINE/HELPFUL			INSPIRING/SUPER FUN		
1	2	3	4	5	6	7	8	9	10

CHAPTER 7.

ROLE-PLAY

INTRODUCTION TO ROLE-PLAY

Role-play can often situate itself within the world of fantasies when it comes to our sexuality, but now it's time to get a little freakier.

Our fantasies can be anything from things we'd like to see our partner wear, to specific ways we've never told them we want them to f*ck us, to situations and scenarios created in our mind that we wish didn't turn us on so much, but they always do…Role-play, on the other hand, is much more literal and much more kink-based as a whole.

To enter into role-playing is to take on the persona of a sexual being other than yourself, which entails treating your partner differently than you normally would and receiving behavior in return from your partner that is out of character - the point is to act. To step outside of ourselves in this way, we must first get to know ourselves, which is why this section has come only at this point in the book. To step into role-playing, you must be aware of both your and your partner's fantasies, desires, and turn-ons. Does your partner crave domination or submission? Do they desire romance or kink? Slow sensuality or rough f*cking, or both? Who are their celebrity crushes? What are their dirty little secrets?

Once you've discovered all the answers to these questions and more in your partner, then you can start to step outside of yourselves in your sex life and start introducing others, through role-play. Put on different hats, see how it feels for you to play a certain character your partner has always yearned for, and find out how it feels to pleasure them through the mind of someone else. It can be very fun to see how we respond to different roles our partner may play, and even more, fun to see what comes out of ourselves when we try to play these roles. You may have several "Whoa, I didn't know that character was inside me" moments, and you may learn of entirely new fetishes, kinks, and turn-ons of your own through acting in a sexual role.

So, give it a shot! All those high school drama classes weren't for nothing!

BEFORE ENTERING THE SECOND HALF OF THIS BOOK, LET'S JUST HAVE A NOTE ON SAFETY.

It is important when entering into any sexual practice to agree on a way of communicating prior to beginning something so that you and your partner can stay on the same page the whole way through and can check in with one another.

This is especially important when practicing kink-based sex. Before entering into role-playing, agree on a safe word between the two of you.

This can be anything at all, but this will be the word that either of you can say at any time during the sexual experience, to tell your partner "Hey, that's too far" or "Hey, I need you to stop." Some common examples of this are the "red, yellow, green" rule (red meaning stop, yellow meaning slow down, green meaning continue) or perhaps choosing a fruit or vegetable to indicate "stop," because these are not common words that would otherwise come up during sex.

It is important to use something that would be out of context and easily recognizable so that the communication can be quick and clear when it needs to be. Discuss safety in general before committing to any practice, decide on your parameters, and then explore each other in the beautiful world of kink and role-play.

After all, safety is sexy!

49

DARLING, IF
YOU LOVE ME

First things first, let's get the giggles out of the way. Oftentimes, the hardest part of role-playing is committing to the role, staying in character, and accessing your inner kink persona.

It's okay to giggle and to make it playful and silly, but there must also be an element of seriousness in your role to get into it with your partner and seduce them in your act.

For this reason, we begin with an old improv game that helps practice keeping a poker face, *Darling, If You Love Me*.

THE PRACTICE

Choose who will be the seducer and who will be "Darling." The objective of the seducer is to make their partner laugh, or at the very least crack a smile - break their poker face. The objective of Darling is to keep a poker face.

The seducer will approach Darling, saying, as the base of the script but not limited to:

"Darling, if you love me, won't you please, please smile?"

Darling then, without even so much as cracking a grin, must respond:

"Darling, you know I love you, but I just can't smile."

It seems relatively simple, and it is, but the key is to make it impossible for your partner to maintain their poker face, so the seducer can get really creative and comical about their approach to their partner.

Or, the seducer can get extremely kinky, and approach their Darling that way.

Consider different ways you can crack their poker face or make it impossible for them to reply with a straight face. Maybe you go the comedy route, and you employ a specific voice that you know cracks them up.

Or maybe you go the sexy route and you spread their legs and give them the most amazing cunnilingus of their life, so they can't possibly get through the sentence they're meant to say. However, that you decide to go about things, consider the things you know your partner can't resist and use them to your advantage.

If Darling laughs, Darling has to pleasure their seducer in whatever way the seducer asks for at least ten minutes. If Darling does not laugh, the seducer has to pleasure their Darling for as long as Darling wishes.

RECORD & REFLECT

Here is your space to reflect on this practice as a couple.
Take some time, be honest, and answer truthfully.

What was the main takeaway/lesson from this practice?

_____

_____

_____

_____

What did you like about this practice?

_____

_____

_____

_____

What was most challenging about this practice?

_____

_____

_____

_____

RATE THIS PRACTICE:

BORING/UNPLEASANT				FINE/HELPFUL			INSPIRING/SUPER FUN		
1	2	3	4	5	6	7	8	9	10

50
FREAKY FRIDAY (SWITCHING ROLES)

Do you remember that iconic early 2000s Lindsay Lohan film, the one where a teenage Lohan switches bodies with her mother (played by Jamie Lee Curtis) and they have to go about their life as one another for the duration of the film? Let's try this in the bedroom - but please don't invite your mother!

THE PRACTICE

You and your partner are going to switch roles, completely, when engaging in any sexy activity, this means that you will entirely adopt one another's methods of seduction, the positions they usually take vs. yourself, and if they're usually dominant or submissive, you will swap them for your own regular role/ behavior. Consider details such as:

- Who usually initiates things?
- Where do they usually touch you first?
- Do they like to boss you around? Or are you usually the one making the orders?
- Who usually gets off first?
- Are there specific things your partner always says to you in bed?
- Names that they call you?
- Do they dirty talk more, or do you?

You can even go as far as considering who, if anyone, usually wears the condom, or who usually has a toy used on them, and switch these things up (yes, there are female condoms).

If one of you often likes some anal play, acting as them, see if you can give this a shot if it's not usually your thing. Fully step into one another's sexual shoes and do your best to get past the gendered nature of many sexual roles, have fun going way outside your comfort zone, and see how you can take on their persona.

RECORD & REFLECT

Here is your space to reflect on this practice as a couple.
Take some time, be honest, and answer truthfully.

What was the main takeaway/lesson from this practice?

_____

_____

_____

_____

What did you like about this practice?

_____

_____

_____

_____

What was most challenging about this practice?

_____

_____

_____

_____

RATE THIS PRACTICE:

BORING/UNPLEASANT				FINE/HELPFUL			INSPIRING/SUPER FUN		
1	2	3	4	5	6	7	8	9	10

51

THE FIRST TIME WE MET FAN FICTION

Here's your chance to rekindle the magic (or the awkwardness, or the drunkenness, or whatever the experience was like) from the first time you and your partner met. Get a little nostalgic with this one, but also a little creative and a little kinky, and re-write it as a "naughty edition."

THE PRACTICE

Go back in your mind to the first time the two of you met. Consider the setting, the circumstance, the way you were feeling, and everything that contributed to the who, what, where, when, why, and how of the beginning of your story. How were you different then? How different was your partner?

You can go as far as setting up a date at that same restaurant where you shared your first meal, or you can simply re-enact the experience from the comfort of your home. Now the "fan fiction" part can come into play; you're going to kink up this night as you would kink up *Twilight* or any other story when writing erotic fan fiction.

Now, without the nerves and awkwardness of meeting for the first time, though still pretending you're meeting for the first time, how would you change the way this experience played out? If you were at a restaurant, would you have rubbed your hand up your partner's thigh? Would you have reached down into their pants very discreetly if you were at the movies? Would you have pulled them into the bathroom and f*cked them up against the wall if you were in a bar? Would you simply have taken them home and tied them to your bedframe? Where does your mind wander when you consider how things *would* have gone, were you not so nervous and there were no "first date social norms" to uphold?

Write the fan fiction about your first date! There are no filters on this date: Surprise one another!

RECORD & REFLECT

Here is your space to reflect on this practice as a couple.
Take some time, be honest, and answer truthfully.

What was the main takeaway/lesson from this practice?

_____

_____

_____

_____

What did you like about this practice?

_____

_____

_____

_____

What was most challenging about this practice?

_____

_____

_____

_____

RATE THIS PRACTICE:

BORING/UNPLEASANT				FINE/HELPFUL			INSPIRING/SUPER FUN		
1	2	3	4	5	6	7	8	9	10

52

"AND YOU ARE?"

This time we'll rekindle the magic of that first meeting, but as though it never even happened. I encourage you to take this one out into public, as this always adds a layer of tension, a layer of realness to your role-play. The innocent bystanders of the public have no idea what is going on between the two of you, and this makes for a more believable scenario.

THE PRACTICE

Choose a location as a place to meet, and give a time and a date to be there, but other than that do not communicate about your plans other than to ensure you'll both be there.

Choose an environment that is easily sociable, perhaps a bar or a park or an event of some kind. The key is that, once you arrive, it'll be as if you've never met before.

On the day of, if possible, spend the day apart, and show up at your agreed-upon location separately. Dress to impress, to make an unforgettable first impression.

Once you arrive, pretend you are single and simply enjoying the atmosphere alone. If it's a bar, whoever shows up first gets a drink and acts as they would if there alone.

Perhaps they strike up a conversation with someone at the bar, chat with the bartender, or play a game of pool, whatever feels natural.

When your partner shows up, don't go over to them right away. Let them enter at their own pace as well. Let them go about their getting a drink, socializing, flirting, etc. And then after some time, approach them as though they're an attractive stranger you'd love to take home and undress. Flirt with them as though you've never met, seduce them ferociously, make their mouth water with this single-and-ready-to-mingle version of you, and make them fall for you all over again.

If their seduction tactics work, take them home, or let them take you home, get into the bedroom, and go at each other in ways that are outside of your routine. F*ck them like you'll never see them again, with the no-holds-barred energy of a one-night-stand.

If you want, you can even go as far as kicking them out after sex, as you would a stranger, or you can let them cuddle for the night and then "slip out" early in the morning. If you live together, you can choose how you handle the "morning after." Do you make them make the walk of shame out to the couch? Do you send them for coffee when you wake?

See how the lust builds in the newness of meeting your partner again, abandon all your expectations and what you know of them, and see how they surprise you!

RECORD & REFLECT

Here is your space to reflect on this practice as a couple.
Take some time, be honest, and answer truthfully.

What was the main takeaway/lesson from this practice?

_____

_____

_____

_____

What did you like about this practice?

_____

_____

_____

_____

What was most challenging about this practice?

_____

_____

_____

_____

RATE THIS PRACTICE:

BORING/UNPLEASANT				FINE/HELPFUL			INSPIRING/SUPER FUN		
1	2	3	4	5	6	7	8	9	10

53

TAKE THE LEAD/POWER PLAY

Now we can start to feel how kinky you really are, let's get into some BDSM-inspired power play. Prior to engaging in this practice, however, have a clear conversation with your partner about whether or not it would be okay with them if you sprung this on them at some point.

Ensure that there is consent, even in surprises. Recall safe words.

THE PRACTICE

First things first, let this one come as a surprise to your partner, catch them off guard. For this one, you do not have to decide beforehand who will be in which role because the idea of the practice is to "take the lead."

Choose a moment when you're feeling empowered, maybe even change into clothing that makes you feel more dominant/assertive, and find your partner in a neutral moment, watching TV or taking a shower or something mundane.

Step fully into the role of the dominant, the master, the top, or however you want to refer to yourself as taking the lead. Decide on your persona, commit to it, and then go out and show your new self to your partner. Before they know it, they are going to be your opposite, your toy (slave, sub, bottom, etc.).

Approach them with force and interrupt whatever they're doing. Make them turn all their attention to you, and demand what you want.

Maybe you interrupt them physically, coming up behind them and engaging in erotic asphyxiation (gentle erotic choking) or perhaps grabbing their hands and holding them above their head or behind their back and pulling them into the bedroom where you'll throw them on the bed and tie their hands back.

Maybe you're verbal at first, making demands of them such as "Turn off the TV, take off your shirt, get on your knees," and so on. Tell them, and show them, that you're in control, that they are to submit to you at this moment. You can try calling them names like "slave, bad boy/girl, my pet" or other names that indicate their submission, then in the role of your dom role, take matters into your own hands and guide them through the sexual experience you want from them.

Have a plan. How are you going to restrain them if you want to practice bondage? How are you going to position them if you want oral sex from them? Show them you know exactly what you want from them, that you're completely in control and do not need their input.

See if you can push yourself to ask for exactly what you want. They're just along for the ride. If it's their pleasure that you want, then make them beg you for it. Find a voice/angle that makes you feel confident and pleasures you both, but ultimately let this be your time to take full control.

RECORD & REFLECT

Here is your space to reflect on this practice as a couple.
Take some time, be honest, and answer truthfully.

What was the main takeaway/lesson from this practice?

_____

_____

_____

_____

What did you like about this practice?

_____

_____

_____

_____

What was most challenging about this practice?

_____

_____

_____

_____

RATE THIS PRACTICE:

BORING/UNPLEASANT				FINE/HELPFUL			INSPIRING/SUPER FUN		
1	2	3	4	5	6	7	8	9	10

54

"TAKE ME OUT TONIGHT"

This time you both get to play completely different characters, together, and take it into public! See how believable you can be to the unassuming bystanders of your kinky games.

THE PRACTICE

Together, decide on characters you'd like to play that have a dynamic that turns you both on for a date night. The key is that these characters have to be very different from your usual self, for both of you, but it has to make sense as to why you're together.

IDEAS

- Maybe we're doing a Mr. and Mrs. Smith situation, and you're both secret agents.
- A big-time CEO and their secretary.
- An Australian tourist and your partner is a local person showing you around.
- An artist and their muse.
- A professor and their eager student.
- A sales rep trying to push their product on a potential customer.

Whatever the choice is, commit to it.

Then, take it out into public and see if you can make it believable. Head somewhere social, maybe just aimlessly out into the city to spend the day, maybe to a specific event or party, or maybe just out for dinner.

See if you can commit to your roles both to each other and to the public throughout your date. If you've adopted an accent (why not?), see if you can maintain it for the entire night, including heading back home and all through sexy time.

The persona you've chosen is you for the entire evening through to the end. How would this person flirt? What would they order to eat? How would they f*ck, or make love?

It can be as mundane or as extravagant a role/scenario as you choose, but whatever it is, commit to it right down to what they would wear and how they would talk to others outside of your partner.

After all, you're not just convincing your partner with this one, you're using your conviction of the public to *help* convince your partner.

RECORD & REFLECT

Here is your space to reflect on this practice as a couple.
Take some time, be honest, and answer truthfully.

What was the main takeaway/lesson from this practice?

_____

_____

_____

_____

What did you like about this practice?

_____

_____

_____

_____

What was most challenging about this practice?

_____

_____

_____

_____

RATE THIS PRACTICE:

BORING/UNPLEASANT				FINE/HELPFUL			INSPIRING/SUPER FUN		
1	2	3	4	5	6	7	8	9	10

55

"I WOULD NEVER"

This one is going to ask you to deliberately step way out of your comfort zone, and for your partner to help you go there. What are your big "no's" and "never in a million years" sexual situations? What doors have you put a "do not enter" sign on for your partner?

What has always been off the table? We all have boundaries and hard no's, and that's okay, but this practice will ask you to question why those strict boundaries have been placed where they are, and how it could maybe actually be quite fun to taste the forbidden fruit.

THE PRACTICE

This time, you're playing a version of yourself that lives in the shadows, the Jekyll to your Hyde, the mischievous little character on your shoulder that wants to spite all of your rules and regulations.

Have a brainstorming session with your partner and write out all of the things you've always refused to try sexually.

FOR EXAMPLE:

- I would never let someone pee on me.
- I would never have anal sex.
- I would never have a threesome.
- I would never have sex with the lights on.
- I would never have sex in public.
- I would never let my partner use a strap on me.
- I would never be submissive.

Whatever they may be, no matter how far out or simple, add them to the list. Some people simply refuse to take their shirt off during sex, due to body insecurities. It's all okay, it's all normal, but we're here to dismantle those walls.

Then, go through the list with your partner and try at least three from each of your lists over time. This does NOT have to be all at once—that may be too overwhelming—but see if you can choose a couple that you'd be interested in trying, either just for laughs or to see if you'd enjoy it. Sometimes we place hard no's on things that we are actually scared of enjoying.

Explore this fearless version of yourselves together! Let your shadow out!

RECORD & REFLECT

Here is your space to reflect on this practice as a couple.
Take some time, be honest, and answer truthfully.

What was the main takeaway/lesson from this practice?

_____

_____

_____

_____

What did you like about this practice?

_____

_____

_____

_____

What was most challenging about this practice?

_____

_____

_____

_____

RATE THIS PRACTICE:

BORING/UNPLEASANT				FINE/HELPFUL			INSPIRING/SUPER FUN		
1	2	3	4	5	6	7	8	9	10

56
CHARACTER PLAY

We all have those movie characters that we would just love to try on for a night, whether it be Zorro or Sandra Dee, and this is your time to make them part of your sex life. This is similar to the *Fantasy Scenes/Scenarios* practice from the last section, but this time we're focused less on the scene and more on the characters.

THE PRACTICE

Decide on characters together that you both know and are familiar with, and ideally that turn both of you on. They don't have to be related, but they can be if it works out and makes sense.

Maybe you both have an affection for Superman, and then in this case you can be Superman and Lex Luthor, Superman and Judge Judy, or Superman and Lois Lane, whatever makes sense to satisfy the desires of both partners simultaneously. Whatever creates the sexiest dynamic for you.

Get fully into costume and get dirty! The specifics of this practice are that you are adopting a pre-determined character, rather than designing your own new role for yourself.

You have to seduce your partner in the way this character would, within the established relationship between the two characters, if they relate, and if they don't, then how would they relate, should they come together?

This can be silly, or kinky, depending on which way you go and how seriously you're able to get into character. Uncover your hidden acting skills, my sexual deviants!

RECORD & REFLECT

Here is your space to reflect on this practice as a couple.
Take some time, be honest, and answer truthfully.

What was the main takeaway/lesson from this practice?

_____

_____

_____

_____

What did you like about this practice?

_____

_____

_____

_____

What was most challenging about this practice?

_____

_____

_____

_____

RATE THIS PRACTICE:

BORING/UNPLEASANT				FINE/HELPFUL			INSPIRING/SUPER FUN		
1	2	3	4	5	6	7	8	9	10

57

PAINT ME LIKE ONE OF YOUR FRENCH GIRLS

There's a reason why so many painters end up romantically entangled with their muses; it's extremely intimate to study someone deeply enough to paint them. In this practice, you are assigned roles to play, and you're going to make art together.

THE PRACTICE

Choose who will be the artist and who will be the muse, choose your medium of choice (paint or pencil), and set up your space so it feels like an artist's studio.

The artist is to produce a nude impression of their muse, which gives the artist full artistic direction of their muse, and the muse is to simply be studied, absorbed, and re-produced by their artist. Muse, strip down to your birthday suit and let your artist position you as they wish. Relax, settle into your body in your new position, and do your best to hold still. Take instruction carefully, really sink in, and get comfy - you'll be here for a while.

Artist, give them a position that will be sustainable to hold for an extended time, but get creative, and get kinky if you wish. Do you want them simply laid out on the couch like a renaissance woman, or do you want their legs spread wide? Do you want them in bondage and physically unable to move, or do you want them comfy, relaxed, and natural sitting by the window? This is your vision, your art - how do you want to capture your muse?

Then, create! Feel the tension build as the muse feels the artist's eyes on them, as you are studied, watched, and turned into art. Artist, as you study your muse, really take inventory of every detail of how they look in this moment - how the light is hitting them, the unique curves and rolls in their skin, the emotion in their eyes. Capture it all.

RECORD & REFLECT

Here is your space to reflect on this practice as a couple.
Take some time, be honest, and answer truthfully.

What was the main takeaway/lesson from this practice?

_____

_____

_____

_____

What did you like about this practice?

_____

_____

_____

_____

What was most challenging about this practice?

_____

_____

_____

_____

RATE THIS PRACTICE:

BORING/UNPLEASANT				FINE/HELPFUL			INSPIRING/SUPER FUN		
1	2	3	4	5	6	7	8	9	10

58
"WHAT IF I..."

Let's play with hypotheticals. Hypothetical speaking is always fun because it allows us to express things that may feel far-fetched but that we may very well secretly want.

It allows us to explore possibilities as though we aren't limited by factors of reality (money, location, gender, social norms, etc.) that usually cause us to revert to the safety of logic. Let your mind wander far and wide. It's hypothetical anyway...or is it?

THE PRACTICE

We're going to employ some of our dirty talk techniques now.

Start by seducing your partner to a point where you're already engaged in foreplay. This works best if you're already pleasuring your partner with your hands.

Once they're already quite turned on both mentally and physically, start considering hypotheticals, and ask your partner while pleasuring them questions that begin with "What if I..."

FOR EXAMPLE:

You're slowly rubbing your fingers around your partner's clit and occasionally putting a finger or two inside them. They're already physically aroused and deeply engaged in the pleasure, and then you ask, "What if I blindfolded you, so you didn't know what was coming?" or perhaps "What if I filmed you while I rub your p*ssy like this?" You can make it as simple or as extravagant as you want: "What if you were my prisoner, and I kept you to f*ck whenever I want?" or "What if I put my dildo inside your ass while I rub you like this?"

The partner being pleasured then has to reply in the same manner, answering the question with another "What if I" question, and form complete sentences. No matter how hard it is to speak while your partner pleasures you, you have to answer the question with another question based on what you would do or how you would feel in response to the initial statement.

FOR EXAMPLE:

When asked "What if I put my dildo inside your ass while I rub you like this?" you could reply "What if I squirted all over you?" When asked "What if you were my prisoner, and I kept you to f*ck whenever I want?" you could reply "What if I was a bad boy/girl and tried to escape?"

The partner pleasuring them, would then reply with another "What if I" question, and the hypothetical situation will build from there. Notice the things you say that really turn your partner on and excite them and the things that don't do as much for them. See if you can bring them to the point of orgasm by speaking in these hypothetical roles you've created together.

Then, next time you start getting freaky, see about turning your hypothetical scenario into a reality!

RECORD & REFLECT

Here is your space to reflect on this practice as a couple.
Take some time, be honest, and answer truthfully.

What was the main takeaway/lesson from this practice?

_____

_____

_____

_____

What did you like about this practice?

_____

_____

_____

_____

What was most challenging about this practice?

_____

_____

_____

_____

RATE THIS PRACTICE:

BORING/UNPLEASANT				FINE/HELPFUL			INSPIRING/SUPER FUN		
1	2	3	4	5	6	7	8	9	10

59

FETISH ARCHETYPES

In case you've been dying to get into the classic, cheesy, 1970s porn archetypes, this one is for you! Think tacky Halloween costumes, think naughty schoolgirl, think MILF/DILF fetish, think avoiding a speeding ticket because "there must be something you can do, officer…" — these sexy archetypes stand the test of time because they're simple and familiar to us all, and well because they're sexy as heck.

THE PRACTICE

Lean into your personal fetishes for this one, consider something mundane that really turns you on. Choose an archetype that feels silly but also sexy for both of you, that fulfills this fetish, and assign roles.

FOR EXAMPLE:

Perhaps you have an oral fixation, and always find yourself turned on when you think about someone's hands in your mouth, putting things in your mouth, etc. So, for the orally enthusiastic person, maybe you're going to the dentist - your partner is the dentist, and they give you an "oral exam" first with their fingers, then with their cock.

Perhaps you're really into the punishment thing, so you're the bad boy speeding around in his sports car and your partner pulls you over. You beg them not to give you a ticket, so instead, you let them punish f*ck you in the backseat of the cruiser.

Get cheesy! It's fun!

RECORD & REFLECT

Here is your space to reflect on this practice as a couple.
Take some time, be honest, and answer truthfully.

What was the main takeaway/lesson from this practice?

_____

_____

_____

_____

What did you like about this practice?

_____

_____

_____

_____

What was most challenging about this practice?

_____

_____

_____

_____

RATE THIS PRACTICE:

BORING/UNPLEASANT				FINE/HELPFUL			INSPIRING/SUPER FUN		
1	2	3	4	5	6	7	8	9	10

60
ALTER EGO

If we let it, we all have a sexual alter ego just dying to come out and take over every now and again. Let's see what happens if we really develop a relationship with them, if we let them fully let their freak flag fly.

THE PRACTICE

Think about who your sexual self is in your head, the one that gets buried by various layers of social constructing of sex and sexuality.

Think about your unfiltered sexual self in different metaphors and layers:

- If your sexual self was a color, what color would it be?
- If your sexual self was an animal, what animal would it be?
- If your sexual self was a genre of music, what genre would it be?
- If your sexual self was an element, what element would it be?
- Is there a particular song that represents your sexual self?
- Is there a particular space where you feel most like your sexual self?
- What would your sexual self, want to wear?
- Who are they attracted to?
- How do they like to f*ck?
- How do they like to be f*cked?
- What does their voice sound like?

Then, give your sexual self a name. It can be anything you like, so long as it feels representative of your unfiltered sexual self. You can pull this name from the questions above, so maybe you're "Red Dragon" or "Water Punk," or maybe it's something different altogether.

Once your alter ego has a name and a persona, introduce them to your partner.

Start slow, and quite literally, introduce them:

"Hi, I'm Water Punk, I'm a sensitive little masochist and I like to be punished when I'm a bad boy."

See how your partner responds and be patient as they navigate getting to know your alter ego.

Then, see how it feels to have sex in this character, in this newly unleashed body and mind of yours that always existed inside of you.

RECORD & REFLECT

Here is your space to reflect on this practice as a couple.
Take some time, be honest, and answer truthfully.

What was the main takeaway/lesson from this practice?

_____

_____

_____

_____

What did you like about this practice?

_____

_____

_____

_____

What was most challenging about this practice?

_____

_____

_____

_____

RATE THIS PRACTICE:

BORING/UNPLEASANT				FINE/HELPFUL			INSPIRING/SUPER FUN		
1	2	3	4	5	6	7	8	9	10

CHAPTER 8.

KINK

INTRODUCTION TO KINK

Kink is one of those words that either excites the shit out of us or scares the shit out of us, there doesn't seem to be much in between. In fact, many folks find kink scary simply because they fear their underlying attraction to it, their desire for it.

This fear is rooted in stigma, especially for women-identifying people, in a society that tells us we must be "good girls" that are soft and delicate and sexually repressed, to be respectable women. The truth, however, is that sexual repression is a lot more dangerous, both to us and to our partners than sexual liberation and kink ever could be. To practice kink, one must be very aware of themselves as well as their partners, able to trust their partner fully, and, dare I say it again, able to communicate, to explore the beautiful world of kink.

If it's not for you then, hey, it's not for you, and that's totally okay, but I'll invite you to dabble in this chapter and these practices to follow with abandonment of your fear of your own pleasure. Pleasure is your birthright! You deserve to explore all aspects of what pleases you; you deserve to know your sexual self fully, without shame or stigma holding you back.

Recall your safe word practice and have a conversation about why you may feel intimidated by kink before starting, and then dive in together with open minds and open legs. We've dabbled in the world of kink now and again throughout this book so far through other practices. Now it's time to take the plunge.

61
BECOMING THE DOM

Have you ever felt that deep within you, there may be a dom/dominatrix banging on the walls of their cage, begging to be unleashed? Does it feel powerful for you to be in control?

Have you struggled to share your desires because you don't want to scare your partner or be too demanding, and yet continue to battle a voice in your head during sex that wants to hold your partner down and take what you want, wants them to fully submit to you?

Reading this, are you getting excited?

Becoming the dom is hard, mostly because it seems like the sexual experience falls all in your hands. It is much easier to submit and give up control as a sub because this allows us to sit back and enjoy. The reality is that the dom is the sub to the sub - when you break it down.

The sub sets the boundaries of what they are okay with from the dom, and within these parameters, the dom will take the reins. To be handed the reins by your partner is to be handed their trust. They trust you and your desires, and now you must trust that wild animal inside you to come out and play.

So, you want to become the dom? Let's start by finding your voice.

THE PRACTICE

One of the most common adaptations of BDSM dynamics between partners is the Master/Slave relationship. Assigning these titles gives us an easy understanding of our roles and can be a simple way to take the plunge into your new dom/dominatrix personas.

You can start either in the bedroom or outside of it; it's up to you! Sometimes it's nice to have a space designated for kink play, but it can happen anywhere.

Dress in attire that makes you feel powerful and in control. Let your partner know when the practice is starting by saying, "I am your master now."

Tell them to strip down as much as you like. If you'd prefer them fully nude or if you'd like them to keep something on in particular, tell them how you want them to look for you.

Next, tell them to get on their knees. This establishes the Master/Slave dynamic commencing.

Sit yourself down on a couch or the side of the bed and tell your slave to crawl toward you on their hands and knees, slowly. As they crawl, talk to them as the slave, saying things like "That's a good little slave, you're going to please me, aren't you? You're going to do whatever I want you to do, you dirty little slave, aren't you?" Use your words to assert your power and their compliance.

Once they get close enough to you, demand a foot massage. You can have them do whatever you want here while you enjoy the pleasure. Have them suck on your toes, and tell them to use massage oil - whatever you want to get the most out of the foot massage.

When you're satisfied with your massage, instruct them on what you want next. See how you can continue in your role through whatever comes to your mind following this initiation into the Master.

RECORD & REFLECT

Here is your space to reflect on this practice as a couple.
Take some time, be honest, and answer truthfully.

What was the main takeaway/lesson from this practice?

_____

_____

_____

_____

What did you like about this practice?

_____

_____

_____

_____

What was most challenging about this practice?

_____

_____

_____

_____

RATE THIS PRACTICE:

BORING/UNPLEASANT				FINE/HELPFUL			INSPIRING/SUPER FUN		
1	2	3	4	5	6	7	8	9	10

62

BECOMING THE SUB

In the BDSM community, it is a largely shared understanding that the sub is really the dom in many ways. The sub sets the boundaries, and the rules, and most often is the one to decide how they want to be dominated. So, to be the sub, you have to be dominant enough to tell your partner what you want, how far you're okay with them taking things, and to establish your safe word.

The other challenging part about becoming the sub is the complete handing over of power and simply receiving. We are not taught how to be on the receiving end, and often feel like we are not doing enough for our partner when we simply sit back to receive pleasure without immediately feeling the need to return the favor. Your job is to release any guilt you may have and fully surrender to receiving from your partner. This is about you.

So, you want to become the sub, do you? Let's start by handing over the power.

THE PRACTICE

One of the most common adaptations of BDSM dynamics between partners is the Master/Slave relationship. Assigning these titles gives us an easy understanding of our roles and can be a simple way to take the plunge into your new sub/slave persona.

You can start either in the bedroom or outside of it; it's up to you! Sometimes it's nice to have a space designated for kink play, but it can happen anywhere. Dress in attire that you know pleases your partner, maybe their favorite pair of your underwear or maybe you're completely nude. Let your partner know when the practice is starting by standing in front of them and saying, "I am your slave now, master."

Sink down onto your knees, take one of their hands in yours, and kiss it. Let them know you're fully at their service.

Look up to their face, make eye contact, and ask them how you can serve them. "How can I please you, master?"

This doesn't have to be sexual right away. If they aren't able to think of something right away, you can make some offers; you could offer to make them a meal, clean the house for them, run them a bath, give them a massage, dance for them, change into different clothing, or take your clothing off, give them oral sex - whatever you think they'd like in that moment. You know them best!

FOR EXAMPLE:

- "Are you hungry, master? Do you want to watch me cook for you?"
- "You look so tense. Can I massage your shoulders, master?"
- "Can I put your cock in my mouth, master? I just want to please you."

While you serve them, tell them to watch you. Ask them how you're doing and remind them that you just want to please them, that you just want to make them happy, and that you'd do anything for your master.

FOR EXAMPLE:

- "How am I doing, master? Do you like watching me cook for you?"
- "Where do you want me to touch you, master? How can I make you feel good?"
- "Do you like watching me bend over while I clean, master?"

Make them feel in control, and let them know you only want to serve them. Onward from this initiation, see how you can continue the dynamic, or see if your partner assumes their Master role and starts taking control from here.

RECORD & REFLECT

Here is your space to reflect on this practice as a couple.
Take some time, be honest, and answer truthfully.

What was the main takeaway/lesson from this practice?

_____

_____

_____

_____

What did you like about this practice?

_____

_____

_____

_____

What was most challenging about this practice?

_____

_____

_____

_____

RATE THIS PRACTICE:

BORING/UNPLEASANT				FINE/HELPFUL			INSPIRING/SUPER FUN		
1	2	3	4	5	6	7	8	9	10

63
SENSORY ELIMINATION GAME

An exciting way to heighten sensations during sex is to take away other senses, to eliminate them. To have control over your partner is to have control over what they feel, and what they don't, to as high a degree as has been decided between the two of you. See how it feels to control their sensations, by reminding them that you have control of their pleasure.

THE PRACTICE

Choose who will be the giver and who the receiver for this practice. Then, consider all of the senses (sight, sound, taste, touch, smell), and consider how you could eliminate each of these, one at a time, during sex.

FOR EXAMPLE:

- To eliminate sight, have your partner wear a blindfold.
- To eliminate sound, use earplugs
- To eliminate taste, cover their mouth with tape or a gag.
- To eliminate touch, tie their hands back (if on a bed) or have them stand with their legs apart and tie their hands over their head (if you can attach something to the ceiling to hold their hands).
- To eliminate any smell, have them wear a mask or pinch their nose - just ensure they can breathe through their mouth.

As you start to get freaky, remember that you are the giver, so you get to choose when you give them their senses and when you take them away, and when one is taken away. You get to choose how to give other sensations that may feel more heightened. Play with taking one sense away and then really stimulating another.

FOR EXAMPLE:

If you've blindfolded them, then you can stimulate touch and taste at the same time by putting your cock in their mouth while simultaneously fondling their genitals.

If you've covered their mouth and tied their hands back, but they can see you, then make them watch while you touch yourself in front of them.

If you've covered their ears and nose, use a vibrator on them (so they can't hear it, but they can feel it) and alternate between using your hands on their genitals and then putting your fingers in their mouth so they can taste themselves.

Try out more than one combination of sensory elimination. See if you can play with giving and taking them away all at least once. Can you take all senses away at once, and then f*ck them or pleasure them in some new way?

RECORD & REFLECT

Here is your space to reflect on this practice as a couple.
Take some time, be honest, and answer truthfully.

What was the main takeaway/lesson from this practice?

_____

_____

_____

_____

What did you like about this practice?

_____

_____

_____

_____

What was most challenging about this practice?

_____

_____

_____

_____

RATE THIS PRACTICE:

BORING/UNPLEASANT				FINE/HELPFUL			INSPIRING/SUPER FUN		
1	2	3	4	5	6	7	8	9	10

64

ORAL PLAY/AIR PLAY

In the hands of our partner, we give up control of our body to the degree that we've agreed upon. Oral play and air play can go hand in hand, or can be separated, depending on how far you want to take this thing.

Oral play simply refers to giving your partner access to your mouth, while air play gives them access to your breath, the power to control your breathing.

This can be taken quite far - to the point where you literally give the partner control of your oxygen by wearing an oxygen mask. We'll just start with the basics for the sake of this practice but know that if this excites you, there are many options for you to explore.

AGREE ON A SAFETY SIGNAL BEFORE THIS PRACTICE, AS YOU WILL NOT BE ABLE TO USE WORDS.

THE PRACTICE

Tools needed: gag equipment (gag ball or mouth cover)

Decide who will be the giver and who the receiver, or if you prefer dom/sub or master/slave terminology, adopt whatever roles/titles turn you on the most.

This will be best to start when sex has already begun, but you can also start sex with this if that's exciting to you.

The receiver/sub/slave will get on their knees and make eye contact with their partner, telling them "My mouth is yours," "My breath is yours" or "I breathe for you," if you're comfortable with handing over your breath.

Open your mouth and wait for your partner to fill it.

The giver/dom/master will put an object of choice in their partner's mouth. This could be a gag ball, a dildo, a cloth of some kind, or their own genitals. If they've given over their breath, then once you've filled their mouth, you can cut off their breath.

You can choose to do this either by choking them (wrapping your hand around their neck and squeezing gently from the sides, *not* from the front and back) or pinching their nose, or any other creative way.

Now you have full control over their breath, and you can play with giving them air and withholding it while you f*ck them.

If your genitals are in their mouth, then make them give you oral sex, but let them breathe now and then.

RECORD & REFLECT

Here is your space to reflect on this practice as a couple.
Take some time, be honest, and answer truthfully.

What was the main takeaway/lesson from this practice?

_____

_____

_____

_____

What did you like about this practice?

_____

_____

_____

_____

What was most challenging about this practice?

_____

_____

_____

_____

RATE THIS PRACTICE:

BORING/UNPLEASANT				FINE/HELPFUL			INSPIRING/SUPER FUN		
1	2	3	4	5	6	7	8	9	10

65
BONDAGE

Often when we think of kink, bondage comes to mind right away. There are many different ways bondage can be practiced, from the ancient, sacred practice of Shibari, to good old-fashioned tying of the hands to the headboard.

The key is to decide how restrained you want to be and if you'd rather use rope or rigs and harnesses, and on a position that both turns you on while also not causing lasting injury (unless that's what you want).

For this practice, we'll use rope, but you can venture down the bondage rabbit hole toward more elaborate contraptions if you're feeling inspired after this round.

THE PRACTICE

Tools needed: rope, some sort of rig to tie the rope to (headboard or heavy objects)

Decide who will be the giver and who the receiver.

The giver will lay their partner down on the bed with their arms and legs away from their body like a starfish. Use the rope to tie their hands out toward the corners of the bed, tight enough that they cannot pull their hands away or bend their arms.

Use more rope to tie each of their ankles out toward the bottom corners of the bed, tight enough that they cannot pull their feet away or bend their knees.

Then, once they're secure and unable to move, you can start pleasuring them. Tease them for a while first, maybe pinch their nipples or put your genitals in their mouth, run your fingers up and down their legs, and make them squirm. Then, once juices are flowing, you can start pleasuring their genitals, either with your hands or your mouth or toys if you have them.

Using vibrators on someone that can't move is absolute torture in the best way, and the only thing that will drive them even more wild is to use a vibrator on their genitals while you f*ck them at the same time.

Pleasure them in a way that will drive them crazy not to be able to touch you. And remember, visual pleasure can be just as effective.

If you tie them up and then ride their cock in a way you know drives them wild, for them to not be able to touch you will be torture!

RECORD & REFLECT

Here is your space to reflect on this practice as a couple.
Take some time, be honest, and answer truthfully.

What was the main takeaway/lesson from this practice?

_____

_____

_____

_____

What did you like about this practice?

_____

_____

_____

_____

What was most challenging about this practice?

_____

_____

_____

_____

RATE THIS PRACTICE:

BORING/UNPLEASANT				FINE/HELPFUL			INSPIRING/SUPER FUN		
1	2	3	4	5	6	7	8	9	10

66
MAKE ME BEG

This practice will recall our *Teasing/Edging* practice from previous, but with a kinkier twist. There is nothing that builds tension like having to beg.

THE PRACTICE

Enter into your dom/sub roles and engage in sex in any kink-based way we've explored this far (bondage, sensory elimination, oral play, etc.).

This practice works best when using bondage so that the sub's body is in full control of the dom, but it can be done with other restraints instead or additionally.

Even though you're already having sex, no matter how you're pleasuring your partner, tell them that they are not allowed to reach orgasm until you tell them they can. Simple as that, but it will drive your sub crazy.

When you start pleasuring them, either with a toy, your hands, your mouth, your genitals, or a combination of these things, tell them they are not allowed to cum until you say so.

Tell them that they have to tell you when they're going to cum. If they start getting close, they have to tell you, and if they don't tell you, they'll be in trouble.

When they tell you they're about to cum, you withhold their orgasm, stop pleasuring them, and you make them give you oral sex instead.

Put your genitals in their mouth and make them pleasure you while keeping a hand on their genitals, stroking them, or fingering them softly until you start to feel their orgasm dissipating.

Once you start to feel their body come away from climax, you can start pleasuring them again, but remind them that they are not allowed to cum. Go through this cycle a couple of times, until you're ready to let them orgasm.

After a couple of rounds, when you start to feel them getting close again, or when they tell you they're ready again, tell them to beg for it.

FOR EXAMPLE:

"You want to cum now, don't you? You're so horny for me, aren't you? Do you want to cum? Let me hear you beg. Beg me for it, baby, let me hear you beg me."

The sub will then respond:

"Please master, let me cum, please let me cum."

When the master is ready, they will tell their sub to cum for them: "Okay, cum for me now."

Watch your sub have the most intense orgasm you've ever seen. Feel how waiting for permission enhances pleasure.

RECORD & REFLECT

Here is your space to reflect on this practice as a couple.
Take some time, be honest, and answer truthfully.

What was the main takeaway/lesson from this practice?

_____

_____

_____

_____

What did you like about this practice?

_____

_____

_____

_____

What was most challenging about this practice?

_____

_____

_____

_____

RATE THIS PRACTICE:

BORING/UNPLEASANT				FINE/HELPFUL			INSPIRING/SUPER FUN		
1	2	3	4	5	6	7	8	9	10

67

PUNISHMENT/PAIN PLAY

Pain can be pleasure, darlings. I promise you that pain can be a pleasure.

In general, we tend to avoid discomfort with all of our power, because, well, it's uncomfortable, and we are not very well trained in how to sit with discomfort. What we forget, however, is that often when we indulge in something a little less pleasurable for a while, if we endure, the pleasure can feel all that much better.

Similarly, often when we indulge in pain, it arouses the senses and increases sensation throughout the entire body, and everything is on red alert. This allows for the degree to which we can feel our pleasure to skyrocket, causing much more intense sensation and pleasure during sex.

THE PRACTICE

Tools: vibrator, sensory toys (nipple clamps, cock tie, flogger, pinwheel, any other sensory toy)

This practice can be paired with any other kink practices (bondage, oral play, sensory elimination, etc.) and can either be used to initiate sex or be incorporated once sex has already begun.

Decide on who will be the giver (dom) and who will be the receiver (sub). The dynamic is "punishment" between dom and sub, where the dom is punishing their sub (maybe for reaching climax too quickly or for not doing what the dom asked, or any other scenario) with sex.

The dom will tell their sub to get on the bed and spread their legs and perhaps take this opportunity to apply bondage or a gag, or whatever else is being used, to their sub. Start verbal, reminding your sub that they're in trouble and this is their punishment, saying things like "You've been a bad girl/boy, haven't you?" Then, tell them what you're going to do to them: "I'm going to make you wish you hadn't done that, I'm going to torture you until you scream."

Turn on the vibrator and place it on their genitals in a way that they will not be able to move it during the remainder of the practice. The vibrator should stay on stimulating them by itself, so you can tie it to them, or to another object to hold it in place.

Then, using your sensory toy (nipple clamps, flogger, pinwheel, or other) apply some pain to another part of their body. Applying pain to another part of their body will cause them to focus on the pleasure in their genitals, heightening the sensation.

If using a clamp on some part of their body apply it gently, and then continue to tighten it until it causes *tolerable* pain. If using a flogger, flog them on their torso, low belly, thighs - the meaty parts of their body, until the flesh turns flush (make sure to always have a safe word and communicate so you know if the sensations are too much).

Continue to apply pain to stronger degrees while the vibrator continues to pleasure their genitals, and then once you're ready, you can either relieve them of the pain or continue inflicting pain while you f*ck them until you climax.

RECORD & REFLECT

Here is your space to reflect on this practice as a couple.
Take some time, be honest, and answer truthfully.

What was the main takeaway/lesson from this practice?

_____

_____

_____

_____

What did you like about this practice?

_____

_____

_____

_____

What was most challenging about this practice?

_____

_____

_____

_____

RATE THIS PRACTICE:

BORING/UNPLEASANT				FINE/HELPFUL			INSPIRING/SUPER FUN		
1	2	3	4	5	6	7	8	9	10

68
SPANKO

Spanking can be a really fun way of engaging in pain play that turns sexual, but it also doesn't have to result in sex. Many people practice spanko simply for the release it offers through the sensation of impact. See if you can lean into the pain and find pleasure in being spanked.

It can be extra fun to apply some role-play to this practice, so maybe go back to the role-play practices and choose some characters that turn you on, and then engage in some spanko fun!

THE PRACTICE

Decide on who is the giver (dom) and who is the receiver (sub).

If you're operating in role-play, then play out your roles in a way that justifies the spanking.

FOR EXAMPLE:

You're a professor and your naughty little student didn't complete the homework assignment. To punish them, you take them over your knee.

The dom will sit on a chair or bed, and position their sub over their lap, so the sub's ass is easily accessible to the dom, and the dom has both hands free. The sub's face should be down, and they should be held in a position so they are ready to receive an impact.

Start by gently rubbing the sub's buttocks. Talking to them throughout, telling them why they're being punished, why they were bad, and so on.

Then, when you're ready, use the palm of your hand to spank them on the fleshy part of the buttocks. Start with a softer impact and spank them ten times in a row, then take a break and rub their buttocks gently again. Again, speak softly to them, remind them they were a bad girl/boy, and they deserve their punishment, and then commence spanking once again. This time spank a little harder. Spank ten times, and then give them a break.

Continue for at least five rounds, as this gives the sub enough time to surrender to the pain. Each time you spank them, add a little more force.

See how much your sub can endure. Watch their flesh turn red. When you think they've had enough, you can stop spanking and start pleasuring - and make sure to give them *lots* of pleasure.

RECORD & REFLECT

Here is your space to reflect on this practice as a couple.
Take some time, be honest, and answer truthfully.

What was the main takeaway/lesson from this practice?

_____

_____

_____

_____

What did you like about this practice?

_____

_____

_____

_____

What was most challenging about this practice?

_____

_____

_____

_____

RATE THIS PRACTICE:

BORING/UNPLEASANT				FINE/HELPFUL			INSPIRING/SUPER FUN		
1	2	3	4	5	6	7	8	9	10

69

BUT OF COURSE, SIXTY-NINE

While this practice may situate itself somewhere between kink and foreplay, it would be cruel not to take the opportunity to bring it in here. The good old sixty-nine but make it kinky.

THE PRACTICE

For those less familiar, sixty-nine is an oral sex technique that involves both partners giving and receiving oral sex simultaneously on one another.

For the sake of this practice, however, we're going to kink it up by adding some bondage.

Decide who will be the giver (dom) and who will be the receiver (sub).

The dom will bind their sub to their bed, or whatever space/apparatus the practice will happen on. You may use the bondage tactic from the Bondage Practice, or you can come up with your own.

Get on top of your sub, so that your genitals are at their mouth level, and their genitals are accessible to your mouth and hands. The sub is unable to move, but they can still provide lots of pleasure for their partner.

Give one another oral sex until everyone has reached an orgasm and is satisfied.

RECORD & REFLECT

Here is your space to reflect on this practice as a couple.
Take some time, be honest, and answer truthfully.

What was the main takeaway/lesson from this practice?

_____

_____

_____

_____

What did you like about this practice?

_____

_____

_____

_____

What was most challenging about this practice?

_____

_____

_____

_____

RATE THIS PRACTICE:

BORING/UNPLEASANT				FINE/HELPFUL			INSPIRING/SUPER FUN		
1	2	3	4	5	6	7	8	9	10

70
TEMPERATURE PLAY

Sex is all about sensation, truly, so finding different ways to stimulate the senses can arouse many different energies in the body.

Temperature play can be a cross between pain play and sensory elimination, with any other kink practices involved that you feel called to include. It just adds additional energy to what is already happening!

THE PRACTICE

Choose who will be the giver (dom) and who will be the receiver (sub).

This might take some creativity, but it can also be quite simple. We're playing with extreme temperatures, so you can use whatever inspires you to access hot and cold sensations for your partner. We'll want to alternate between the two.

Start with cold. You can use something very literal, like ice cubes straight to the flesh or going outside into the cold if you live in a cold climate and having your partner endure the cold for a certain amount of time, or you can be gentler and perhaps put a wet cloth into the fridge/freezer, and then lay the cloth over a part of your sub's body.

The idea is to explore how the sensation of cold can recall pain play and have your partner lean into the discomfort.

Immediately after exposing the sub to the cold, you've provided, now it's time to give them heat. This can be direct, like the ice cubes, with hot wax or hot oil for a massage, or you can have them go into a hot space (a sauna, the outdoors if it's really hot outside), maybe a heated blanket, or you can be gentler or a hot water bottle/heating pad placed on their body.

Apply both temperatures to different parts of their body: their stomach, their inner thighs, their feet, their genitals, or their chest.

Apply different sensations to different parts of the body and alternate between body parts and temperatures, and pleasure them with your hands or a toy while you apply temperature play.

Push their ability to stand both extreme cold and extreme heat as you alternate back and forth between hot and cold, stimulating their senses and offering them both pain and pleasure simultaneously. See how their pleasure changes between the different sensations.

RECORD & REFLECT

Here is your space to reflect on this practice as a couple.
Take some time, be honest, and answer truthfully.

What was the main takeaway/lesson from this practice?

_____

_____

_____

_____

What did you like about this practice?

_____

_____

_____

_____

What was most challenging about this practice?

_____

_____

_____

_____

RATE THIS PRACTICE:

BORING/UNPLEASANT				FINE/HELPFUL			INSPIRING/SUPER FUN		
1	2	3	4	5	6	7	8	9	10

71

INTO THE PUBLIC

It can be fun to engage in kinky role-play in the home, but what happens when we take this out into the public? How does it look to adopt your dom/sub or master/slave (or other titles) roles, out in the real world? Can you stay in this dynamic?

THE PRACTICE

Assign roles, and then choose a destination for your date that suits your dynamic. Perhaps you're just going for dinner, or perhaps you'd like to take this out for a shopping day or to a summer carnival.

Maybe you're just going grocery shopping, the choices are completely open. It doesn't necessarily matter where you go, the point is to test your ability to stay in your role, in your dynamic, outside of the bedroom.

Trying to maintain your dynamic outside of the bedroom can spice up the dynamic when you get back to the bedroom with a lot of anticipation and intensity.

FOR EXAMPLE:

You go to a restaurant for dinner, and the dom orders everything for the table, for both themselves and their sub. The sub gets to be spoiled, but also has to eat what they are served.

For this reason, the dom should choose foods that are aphrodisiacs or that they know their sub will enjoy.

If you're going shopping, the dom will pick out garments for the sub to try on that they want to see their sub wear for them.

RECORD & REFLECT

Here is your space to reflect on this practice as a couple.
Take some time, be honest, and answer truthfully.

What was the main takeaway/lesson from this practice?

_____

_____

_____

_____

What did you like about this practice?

_____

_____

_____

_____

What was most challenging about this practice?

_____

_____

_____

_____

RATE THIS PRACTICE:

BORING/UNPLEASANT				FINE/HELPFUL			INSPIRING/SUPER FUN		
1	2	3	4	5	6	7	8	9	10

CHAPTER 9.
COUPLED PORNOGRAPHY

INTRODUCTION TO COUPLED PORNOGRAPHY

Most commonly, pornography is something we indulge in alone, something we feel we have to keep to ourselves and use for our pleasure. Often, we're actually very secretive about our use and enjoyment of pornography.

Pornography is a very powerful tool in the development and engagement of our sexualities both during masturbation as well as within our partnered sexual relationships when used intentionally.

It has the power to inspire us, open our minds, guide us, show us what we want to see, fulfill fantasies we otherwise wouldn't have access to, and much more! When watching porn with our partners, it allows all of these same expansions to happen in our partnered sex.

So, take the plunge together into the creative, adventurous world of coupled pornography. The camera pulls many things out of us that we didn't know were there. Who knows, you could become porn stars yourselves!

72
WHAT DO YOU LIKE?

As porn is something we often consume when we're alone, it's actually quite common for partners not to know what their partner likes in pornography. This is your chance to bring your partner into your erotic little world and show them what you like to watch.

THE PRACTICE

Simple, watch porn together! But first, set the mood. Get in bed, or sit on your partner's lap, light a candle, have a glass of wine, and get into the spirit.

Then, decide who will choose what they like to watch first, and this is the key: You both have to be completely honest about what you like to watch while you're alone. You have to show your partner something that you would watch if it was just you.

Watch whatever is chosen together and see how it makes both of you feel. If it turns you on, let it. If it doesn't do much for you, that's okay.

Then, let the other partner decide on the next piece to watch. At least make sure that both parties have a chance to make a selection, but you can keep going if you like. Have a porn marathon!

RECORD & REFLECT

Here is your space to reflect on this practice as a couple.
Take some time, be honest, and answer truthfully.

What was the main takeaway/lesson from this practice?

_____

_____

_____

_____

What did you like about this practice?

_____

_____

_____

_____

What was most challenging about this practice?

_____

_____

_____

_____

RATE THIS PRACTICE:

BORING/UNPLEASANT				FINE/HELPFUL			INSPIRING/SUPER FUN		
1	2	3	4	5	6	7	8	9	10

73
VIEWING PARTY

For our viewing party, we're going to step outside of our porn norms, operating on the premise that often we are turned on by pornography that we would never expect to be turned on by. A lot of our sexualities are learned.

We are told what we should like and what we should watch, so it can come as a surprise when we are suddenly aroused by something outside of what we normally gravitate toward when trying to get off. This is simply because our sexual selves are so much more complex than we are taught to understand. This time, we're going to open our minds, watch a variety of different genres of porn, and see what hits us!

THE PRACTICE

You and your partner are going to have a viewing party for different genres of pornography that you both don't normally gravitate toward. Have some wine, wear something sexy, dim the lights, and then go onto whatever porn platform you usually use and browse the categories.

Maybe you've never ventured into the more hardcore stuff, maybe it's the MILF stuff that has never popped up on your screen before, or maybe you've never explored Hentai.

Put the categories on shuffle, or maybe just select a couple of different ones you'd be interested in exploring, and then get cozy, nice and close together with your partner and have a viewing party!

See what turns you on and what doesn't. Be open and communicative about what turns you on and what really doesn't work for you. You could be discovering lots of new little kinks and quirks about one another, and yourself! Be open and enjoy!

RECORD & REFLECT

Here is your space to reflect on this practice as a couple.
Take some time, be honest, and answer truthfully.

What was the main takeaway/lesson from this practice?

_____

_____

_____

_____

What did you like about this practice?

_____

_____

_____

_____

What was most challenging about this practice?

_____

_____

_____

_____

RATE THIS PRACTICE:

BORING/UNPLEASANT				FINE/HELPFUL			INSPIRING/SUPER FUN		
1	2	3	4	5	6	7	8	9	10

74
MONKEY SEE
MONKEY DO

Sometimes we watch porn just to get off, sometimes we watch because we want to get ideas for when we have sex with our partners, and sometimes we watch porn because we want to imagine what it would be like to be the people in the videos.

Now is your chance to live the experience, by using porn as your instruction manual.

THE PRACTICE

Together, choose a category that you'd both feel comfortable re-enacting scenes from. Then, within the category of porn, choose a video at random, a video neither of you has ever seen before.

As the video starts, make sure you can both easily see the screen. You are to choose which partner is playing which person in the video, and you are to "monkey see, monkey do," the actors on the screen.

Approach one another exactly as the actors do, touch one another the way the actors do, and follow their moves exactly, verbally repeating the things they say, fully copying their actions as closely as you can.

At some point, you may go off script and get into things, which might cause it to be hard to pay attention. That's okay. The goal is to use the video as a guide and re-enact as close as you can, but ultimately the real goal is to turn one another on, so if going off script works better, then do that! But give the video a fair shot! See how it feels to adopt another's movements on your partner and let yourself be guided by the porn.

RECORD & REFLECT

Here is your space to reflect on this practice as a couple.
Take some time, be honest, and answer truthfully.

What was the main takeaway/lesson from this practice?

_____

_____

_____

_____

What did you like about this practice?

_____

_____

_____

_____

What was most challenging about this practice?

_____

_____

_____

_____

RATE THIS PRACTICE:

BORING/UNPLEASANT				FINE/HELPFUL			INSPIRING/SUPER FUN		
1	2	3	4	5	6	7	8	9	10

75

DIY: AUDIOPORN

Audioporn is its own genre of porn that does not include visual accompaniment; it's all in the ears. It is very popular for folks (especially women) that enjoy a more submissive role, and get turned on by being told what to do, what their partner likes, etc.

Because there is no visual stimulation, it allows one's mind to wander in this area and opens up lots of fantasy in connecting the voice speaking naughty things into your ear, to who you wish the voice to be. So, how do apply this to our partnered sex then? You DIY it!

THE PRACTICE

You're going to make audioporn for your partner. Yep, you're going to get them off with just your voice!

First, it will most likely help to listen to some audioporn before you make your own, just so you can get a feel for the different tones and spins that can be taken.

Most commonly, audioporn will instruct its listener on how to pleasure themselves, and while doing so, the speaker will audibly pleasure themselves.

You can decide how much you want to make it about you, or how much you want to be on the instructional side of things. Take your partner into account. So, they like to watch you get yourself off, or do they like to be told by you what you want them to do to themselves?

You can think back on the *Phone Sex Practice* if that helps you recall how your partner likes to be involved in your masturbation.

FOR EXAMPLE:

You could walk your partner through how you're pleasuring yourself, telling them how you're unbuttoning your pants and sliding your hand between your legs, and how you want them to do the same to themselves, etc.

When you've created your recording, you'll send it to them to listen to when you're not there. Their very own audioporn, made just for them, by the person that turns them on most!

RECORD & REFLECT

Here is your space to reflect on this practice as a couple.
Take some time, be honest, and answer truthfully.

What was the main takeaway/lesson from this practice?

_____

_____

_____

_____

What did you like about this practice?

_____

_____

_____

_____

What was most challenging about this practice?

_____

_____

_____

_____

RATE THIS PRACTICE:

BORING/UNPLEASANT				FINE/HELPFUL			INSPIRING/SUPER FUN		
1	2	3	4	5	6	7	8	9	10

76
DIY: SETTING
A SCENE

Sometimes the sexiest thing about pornography is the setting in which it takes place. So now let's see if we can recreate those sexy moods and make our porn! And no, I'm not talking about the shag rugs and velvet couches of the classic 70s porno setting. Unless that's your thing, in which case, go for it!

THE PRACTICE

Choose a piece of pornography that turns both you and your partner on equally. Consider where it takes place. Is it in a massage parlor? Is it in a doctor's office? A bedroom? A dungeon? What about the setting contributes to the sexy energy that gets you going?

Then, see if you can recreate the scene in your home, with what you have. Can you make your living room feel like a massage parlor or a strip club?

Can you make your bedroom feel like a dungeon? Have some fun playing around to re-create the sexy porn scene, then make a sex tape!

Prop a recording device somewhere in the space where it can catch both the ambiance as well as the two of you getting freaky, then film yourselves getting sexy in your new space!

BONUS

Add your DIY pornography from this practice to your *Viewing Party* roster!

RECORD & REFLECT

Here is your space to reflect on this practice as a couple.
Take some time, be honest, and answer truthfully.

What was the main takeaway/lesson from this practice?

_____

_____

_____

_____

What did you like about this practice?

_____

_____

_____

_____

What was most challenging about this practice?

_____

_____

_____

_____

RATE THIS PRACTICE:

BORING/UNPLEASANT				FINE/HELPFUL			INSPIRING/SUPER FUN		
1	2	3	4	5	6	7	8	9	10

77

DIY: POV

POV (Point of View) is another very widely enjoyed category of pornography on many pornography platforms. It is a very close-up, involved type of porn, where the actors in the film hold the camera and film things from their point of view.

THE PRACTICE

In creating DIY POV porn, you're going to get nice and intimate with the camera. While you're having sex, you'll take turns filming one another, right amid the action!

Play with different angles and catch one another's facial reactions as well as other parts of the body, all while switching positions to keep a diverse and playful viewing experience.

Get your partner on film from all the angles you love to watch them during sex.

Also, have fun performing for the camera! Get a little cheeky; winking or saying things into the camera can make for a really sexy playback experience, and it can make things at the moment feel extra juicy as well. You may surprise yourself and your partner with what you can serve up when on camera—maybe you're an exhibitionist!

BONUS

Add your own DIY pornography from this practice to your *Viewing Party* roster!

RECORD & REFLECT

Here is your space to reflect on this practice as a couple.
Take some time, be honest, and answer truthfully.

What was the main takeaway/lesson from this practice?

_____

_____

_____

_____

What did you like about this practice?

_____

_____

_____

_____

What was most challenging about this practice?

_____

_____

_____

_____

RATE THIS PRACTICE:

BORING/UNPLEASANT				FINE/HELPFUL			INSPIRING/SUPER FUN		
1	2	3	4	5	6	7	8	9	10

78
DIY: CASTING COUCH

Casting Couch is another very widely enjoyed category of porn, which captures the experience of casting porn actors by first interviewing them on the casting couch, and then usually taking them for a whirl and getting sexy to see if they'll make a good porn actor/actress.

In itself, it is a very sexy experience.

THE PRACTICE

You can choose to film this or not; it's completely up to you.

You're going to watch some Casting Couch porn videos, to get a feel for the type of questions the producers ask their candidates, and then you're going to role-play these roles with your partner; one of you being the producer and the other will be the actor/actress auditioning to be in porn films.

Commit to the roles. Have the partner playing the actor/actress enter in to the space and sit down on the couch. Ask them a series of questions:

- What is your name? (Come up with a porn name for yourself)
- How old are you?
- What type of porn do you want to do?

Then you will ask them to pose while you take some sexy photos of them. You'll ask them to strip, to spread their legs so you can examine their p*ssy, etc. Examine their body thoroughly. Then you'll f*ck them, to see how they'll work as a porn actress, of course. It's all business.

RECORD & REFLECT

Here is your space to reflect on this practice as a couple.
Take some time, be honest, and answer truthfully.

What was the main takeaway/lesson from this practice?

_____

_____

_____

_____

What did you like about this practice?

_____

_____

_____

_____

What was most challenging about this practice?

_____

_____

_____

_____

RATE THIS PRACTICE:

BORING/UNPLEASANT				FINE/HELPFUL			INSPIRING/SUPER FUN		
1	2	3	4	5	6	7	8	9	10

CHAPTER 10.

CHEEKY LITTLE GAMES

INTRODUCTION TO CHEEKY LITTLE GAMES

While all of the practices we've explored thus far involve planning and getting really creative and pushing limits and comfort out of the box, sometimes it's nice to get a little sexually playful in ways that aren't as in-depth and intense.

It can be fun just to play flirty little games and get a little cheeky, in a lighter, more humorous experience.

The games in this chapter strive to be simple and accessible, for those times when you're just hanging out and want to be a little cheeky but don't need all of the seriousness and time commitment that comes with the more detailed practices.

Here, we can turn a casual game night into a frisky evening, but all we need is a deck of cards or a couple of dice, things we have laying around the house. And you can play these really anywhere, so you're not limited by your space and surroundings or by energy levels.

So, let's play!

79

BUT MAKE IT STRIP

Anything can be cheeky if you add a "strip" component. This one can be incorporated into any of the games you already play during game night.

THE GAME

It's simple. Whatever games you have laying around in the cupboards or under the coffee table, we're going to spice them up! We're going to play our regular board games - *Risk, Battleship, Trouble, Gin Rummy, Poker*, whatever it may be - but we're going to add "strip" to the stakes.

Depending on the game you're playing, you'll have to decide how incorporating strip makes sense. We're all familiar with strip poker, so if that's your game, then go for it! But if you're more of a *Monopoly* household, then see about incorporating it there. Whenever you pass Go, your partner has to remove a clothing item - things like that.

Come up with your own rules and make your own games a little cheeky!

RECORD & REFLECT

Here is your space to reflect on this practice as a couple.
Take some time, be honest, and answer truthfully.

What was the main takeaway/lesson from this practice?

_____

_____

_____

_____

What did you like about this practice?

_____

_____

_____

_____

What was most challenging about this practice?

_____

_____

_____

_____

RATE THIS PRACTICE:

BORING/UNPLEASANT				FINE/HELPFUL			INSPIRING/SUPER FUN		
1	2	3	4	5	6	7	8	9	10

80
"WOULD YOU RATHER?"

This one can be played anywhere. In its essence, it's a word game. The beauty of that is that you can get cheeky while driving to the grocery store or walking the dog.

You can get into frisky mode outside of the bedroom, and then you can employ your learnings once you get back in there with your lover.

THE GAME

Take turns asking your partner "Would you rather" questions that have to do with your sex life.

FOR EXAMPLE:

- "Would you rather have sex in the shower or sex in the bath?"
- "Would you rather me use a vibrator or just my hands on you?"
- "Would you rather have a threesome with another man or another woman?"
- "Would you rather me approach you fully nude or in lingerie?"

The questions can really be about anything. It's just a fun little way to learn more about your partner sexually.

RECORD & REFLECT

Here is your space to reflect on this practice as a couple.
Take some time, be honest, and answer truthfully.

What was the main takeaway/lesson from this practice?

_____

_____

_____

_____

What did you like about this practice?

_____

_____

_____

_____

What was most challenging about this practice?

_____

_____

_____

_____

RATE THIS PRACTICE:

BORING/UNPLEASANT				FINE/HELPFUL			INSPIRING/SUPER FUN		
1	2	3	4	5	6	7	8	9	10

81

WORD ASSOCIATION

This is a very common word game, and again, it can be played anywhere. The key is to make it a little sexier. Just see where your minds go.

THE GAME

One person starts by saying a word related to sex, and their partner has to respond by saying the first word that comes to their mind in association with that word.

FOR EXAMPLE:

The first partner says "anal" to start. The next partner says "butt plug" to follow. From here, the first partner says "toys," to which their partner responds, "sex shop," and so on.

RECORD & REFLECT

Here is your space to reflect on this practice as a couple.
Take some time, be honest, and answer truthfully.

What was the main takeaway/lesson from this practice?

_____

_____

_____

_____

What did you like about this practice?

_____

_____

_____

_____

What was most challenging about this practice?

_____

_____

_____

_____

RATE THIS PRACTICE:

BORING/UNPLEASANT				FINE/HELPFUL			INSPIRING/SUPER FUN		
1	2	3	4	5	6	7	8	9	10

82
SEXY DECKS

This game can be played with any deck of cards! You might want to do this one at home, or at least in a private space, so you can get into all the cards and their meanings and have fun with them.

THE GAME

Using a standard deck of playing cards:

On a piece of paper, write out the numbers two to ten, and then Ace, Jack, King, and Queen.

Together, assign an action to each card. Then, assign a part of the body to each suit (hearts, clubs, spades, diamonds). Then shuffle the cards thoroughly and deal out each player five to ten cards. Decide on a number together. Both players will keep their cards facing down, and then one at a time will flip them over, taking turns with their partner revealing their cards. Whatever card you turn up, you have to perform it's associated action (from the number) on the associated body part (from the suit) on your partner right then, before the next player takes their turn.

FOR EXAMPLE:

Q	Lick	♦	Chest
K	Suck	♠	Neck
2	Kiss	♥	Torso
3	Caress	♣	Genitals
4	Smack		
5	Bite		

RECORD & REFLECT

Here is your space to reflect on this practice as a couple.
Take some time, be honest, and answer truthfully.

What was the main takeaway/lesson from this practice?

_____

_____

_____

_____

What did you like about this practice?

_____

_____

_____

_____

What was most challenging about this practice?

_____

_____

_____

_____

RATE THIS PRACTICE:

BORING/UNPLEASANT				FINE/HELPFUL			INSPIRING/SUPER FUN		
1	2	3	4	5	6	7	8	9	10

83
KINKY DICE

This game can be played with any regular dice! You might want to do this one at home, or at least in a private space, so you can get into all the roles and their meanings and have fun with them.

THE GAME

You can use one dice or two. The more dice, the more actions and activities are possible to roll, so see how many ideas you have and if you'd like to have more to choose from, or if you two would like to keep practicing things on one another over and over. Both are equally sexy options!

Similar to the cards, assign each number an activity and write them out so you remember all of the numbered meanings, but this time they can be more involved. Take turns rolling, and whatever you roll has to be performed then and there, before the next player takes their turn.

FOR EXAMPLE:

Q	Make out for one minute
K	Suck on your partner's earlobes
2	Take three clothing items off
3	Hand stuff for four minutes
4	Oral sex for five minutes
5	Make your partner cum

RECORD & REFLECT

Here is your space to reflect on this practice as a couple.
Take some time, be honest, and answer truthfully.

What was the main takeaway/lesson from this practice?

_____

_____

_____

_____

What did you like about this practice?

_____

_____

_____

_____

What was most challenging about this practice?

_____

_____

_____

_____

RATE THIS PRACTICE:

BORING/UNPLEASANT				FINE/HELPFUL			INSPIRING/SUPER FUN		
1	2	3	4	5	6	7	8	9	10

84
NEVER HAVE I EVER

This is an old drinking game, but we're going to make it an old *sexy* game. It's another word game, so it can be played anywhere, but it may get your juices flowing, or you may wish to include some elements of the strip, etc., so choose your timing wisely.

THE GAME

Both partners raise three fingers. One partner starts by saying "Never have I ever…" and then they say something sexual that they've never done.

If the other partner has done that thing before, they put a finger down. Now it's the second partner's turn. They will say "Never have I ever…" and then say something sexual they've never done and see if their partner puts a finger down.

The first one to put all three fingers down has to massage their partner wherever their partner wishes for at least ten minutes.

FOR EXAMPLE:

"Never have I ever had a threesome." The other partner puts their finger down, and then takes their turn with "Never have I ever had sex in public," to which their partner doesn't put a finger down because they've also never done that.

BONUS

The things that neither of you has done should be made into a bucket list for the two of you to try together over time.

RECORD & REFLECT

Here is your space to reflect on this practice as a couple.
Take some time, be honest, and answer truthfully.

What was the main takeaway/lesson from this practice?

_____

_____

_____

_____

What did you like about this practice?

_____

_____

_____

_____

What was most challenging about this practice?

_____

_____

_____

_____

RATE THIS PRACTICE:

BORING/UNPLEASANT				FINE/HELPFUL			INSPIRING/SUPER FUN		
1	2	3	4	5	6	7	8	9	10

85
ONE WORD
AT A TIME

This is similar to word association, but this time you're building an erotic story together.

THE GAME

The first person will start by saying one word, and the next partner will respond with another single word, and then the other partner will follow again by adding another word, and the goal is to move in the direction of building an erotic story, one word at a time, together.

FOR EXAMPLE:

The first partner starts with "one," to which the next partner responds "day," and then the first partner says "I," and the other replies "went," "to," "the," "store," "and," "bought," "chocolate," "syrup," "to," "smear," "all," "over," "your," "breasts," and so on.

Build your story together and see where it goes!

RECORD & REFLECT

Here is your space to reflect on this practice as a couple.
Take some time, be honest, and answer truthfully.

What was the main takeaway/lesson from this practice?

_____

_____

_____

_____

What did you like about this practice?

_____

_____

_____

_____

What was most challenging about this practice?

_____

_____

_____

_____

RATE THIS PRACTICE:

BORING/UNPLEASANT				FINE/HELPFUL			INSPIRING/SUPER FUN		
1	2	3	4	5	6	7	8	9	10

86

THE JAR OF DESIRE

This is a game that can take place over a long time, or it can be kept within an evening, a week, or a month - the timespan is yours to decide. Or you might not decide, and let it play out naturally.

THE GAME

Find yourselves a jar and cut some paper into small pieces. Each partner gets between five to ten pieces of paper, and on each piece of paper they'll write out something they desire.

Perhaps it's a foot massage, anal sex, or for their partner to run them a bath or wear something specific. It can be anything but keep it cheeky. Keep it sexy.

Then, put all of the papers into the jar, shake it up, and set it on the nightstand.

Now you have an inventory of sexy ideas/desires to pull from whenever you feel the need to spice things up in the bedroom.

RECORD & REFLECT

Here is your space to reflect on this practice as a couple.
Take some time, be honest, and answer truthfully.

What was the main takeaway/lesson from this practice?

_____

_____

_____

_____

What did you like about this practice?

_____

_____

_____

_____

What was most challenging about this practice?

_____

_____

_____

_____

RATE THIS PRACTICE:

BORING/UNPLEASANT				FINE/HELPFUL			INSPIRING/SUPER FUN		
1	2	3	4	5	6	7	8	9	10

87
SEXY SCAVENGER HUNT

Everyone loves a good scavenger hunt, it's just the truth. Nothing is more exciting than finding a fun game your partner has set up for you, to lead you to a surprise at the end.

It's a fun opportunity for them to put on their thinking hat and think like you, to solve the clues and make it through to claim their prize. Let their prize be you in all your sexy glory!

THE GAME

Choose a time when your partner is out of the house, or perhaps when they're planning to come over to your place if you don't live together. Set up a cheeky scavenger hunt for them to find when they arrive in the space.

The first thing they find should be some sort of note or instructions that explain to them what is going on, and then leads them to the next clue.

You can get as elaborate or as contained with it as you want - leading them all over town for clues, or simply guiding them searching around the bedroom.

Make the clues a little naughty. Maybe with every clue, there's another clothing item you'd like them to put on as they go, or maybe with every clue they find a toy you want them to use on you at the end. You can make it your own but keep it sexy!

After leading them through several clues, let them find you waiting for them either in the bedroom or somewhere else, with a mood set and sexy energy in the air.

RECORD & REFLECT

Here is your space to reflect on this practice as a couple.
Take some time, be honest, and answer truthfully.

What was the main takeaway/lesson from this practice?

_____

_____

_____

_____

What did you like about this practice?

_____

_____

_____

_____

What was most challenging about this practice?

_____

_____

_____

_____

RATE THIS PRACTICE:

BORING/UNPLEASANT				FINE/HELPFUL			INSPIRING/SUPER FUN		
1	2	3	4	5	6	7	8	9	10

88
SEXY TWISTER

It's probably safe to say that we're all familiar with the game *Twister* and that we've all had moments where we've considered how *Twister* could get quite sexy, quite quickly.

But how many of us have actually gone there? Deflowered the game? Dirtied that white plastic mat? How about, my sexually curious friends, we make it sexy!

THE GAME

Find yourself a *Twister* mat. If you can't find one, you can make one!

To make a *Twister* mat on your floor: All you need to DIY a *Twister* mat is some masking tape and markers and space on your floor. Use the masking tape to mark 24 spots in a 6x4 grid on the floor, evenly spaced.

Then, use the markers to color the masking tape so you can at least tell what color it is meant to be. The colors will be in the order - red, blue, yellow, and green. Then, make yourself a spinner wheel with some sort of cardboard, with the colors on it. Voila! You have *Twister*!

Play the game following the regular rules, but you're making it sexy, so you're playing in as little clothing as you're comfortable with. If fully nude is your thing, go for it!

Choose stakes for the game between the two of you: Maybe the loser has to massage the winner or maybe you engage in some kink and do some punishment play. The stakes are yours to decide!

RECORD & REFLECT

Here is your space to reflect on this practice as a couple.
Take some time, be honest, and answer truthfully.

What was the main takeaway/lesson from this practice?

_____

_____

_____

_____

What did you like about this practice?

_____

_____

_____

_____

What was most challenging about this practice?

_____

_____

_____

_____

RATE THIS PRACTICE:

BORING/UNPLEASANT				FINE/HELPFUL			INSPIRING/SUPER FUN		
1	2	3	4	5	6	7	8	9	10

89
DIRTY JENGA

In keeping with the theme of spicing up the games we all know and love, let's see how many opportunities there are to make our game nights dirty with the classic games we already have. Anything can be sexified if you get creative!

THE GAME

You're playing *Jenga*, as usual, but the twist is that you'll write naughty activities or acts to perform on one another, or for one another, on about half of the blocks before you stack them in their tower form.

Then, when you start to play, as each of you pulls blocks, whenever you pull a block with an instruction, you'll be required to complete what is indicated on the block before you move on to the next person's turn.

Whoever knocks the tower over has to serve their partner in some way. Perhaps if you lose, you'll owe your partner an orgasm or a meal. It can be whatever you decide.

RECORD & REFLECT

Here is your space to reflect on this practice as a couple.
Take some time, be honest, and answer truthfully.

What was the main takeaway/lesson from this practice?

_____

_____

_____

_____

What did you like about this practice?

_____

_____

_____

_____

What was most challenging about this practice?

_____

_____

_____

_____

RATE THIS PRACTICE:

BORING/UNPLEASANT				FINE/HELPFUL			INSPIRING/SUPER FUN		
1	2	3	4	5	6	7	8	9	10

90
CODE WORDS

The fun thing about this one is that it can take place in public, at any time, in any place, whenever you feel so inspired.

It's fun to have inside jokes and cheeky little shared secrets within your partnership.

That's how things stay interesting, how you maintain your unique connection, and how you feel deeply intertwined with one another, no matter where you go. It is so important to maintain those little special things between the two of you, that only the two of you really understand.

THE GAME

Come up with some code words, a secret language if you will, to talk about sex with your partner, or at least to indicate sexual thoughts to them, while you're out in public or with friends.

This is so that no one else knows what you're taking about and yet you're able to tell your partner from across the room just how badly you want them.

FOR EXAMPLE:

You decide that "eggplant" means "horny," "honeybee" means "I want to eat your pussy," "treehouse" means "I want to take you home," "boom shakalaka" means "meet me in the bathroom in five minutes," and so on.

It can just be fun to have your own little language!

RECORD & REFLECT

Here is your space to reflect on this practice as a couple.
Take some time, be honest, and answer truthfully.

What was the main takeaway/lesson from this practice?

_____

_____

_____

_____

What did you like about this practice?

_____

_____

_____

_____

What was most challenging about this practice?

_____

_____

_____

_____

RATE THIS PRACTICE:

BORING/UNPLEASANT				FINE/HELPFUL			INSPIRING/SUPER FUN		
1	2	3	4	5	6	7	8	9	10

CHAPTER 11.

NON-SEXUAL PARTNERED INTIMACY

INTRODUCTION TO NON-SEXUAL PARTNERED INTIMACY

While we've been very sex-focused thus far, it is naïve to think that we are just always ready to have sex all the time, at any given moment. We are not sex machines, no matter how much we sometimes wish we were.

There will be days when you're both tired, or when one or both of you are menstruating, or when you've just eaten a giant meal, so you don't feel very sexy and don't want sex at all. And that is okay. It is also okay to still want intimacy and closeness, without wanting sex all of the time, and there is actually a lot of intimacy that comes without sex.

We often link the two in our heads - intimacy and sex - and have a hard time separating them.

This chapter is for those days when you still want intimacy, you want to be held and to be close to your partner, but you don't necessarily want to get freaky in the sheets.

You just want to connect, but less physically, and many options for you will satisfy your desire for connection but won't cause you to feel guilt for not wanting to f*ck 24/7.

You're human, your desire ebbs and flows, and we can ebb and flow with it!

91
MIRROR MASSAGE

When we think of ways to invite partnered intimacy into our relationships, often massage comes to mind, mostly because a good old-fashioned massage never gets old.

This is one of the most connective, timeless practices for intimacy and, truly, the practice can be as traditional and simple as needed to pique your interest. However, I would like to invite you to take this one step further. Explore how it feels to introduce a mirror to your massage.

THE PRACTICE

Position yourselves in front of a mirror large enough that you can see the majority of your bodies with ease, with one partner sitting or standing behind the other, so they are still visible in the mirror.

Start by acknowledging yourself through your reflection visually.

Take yourselves in. How does it feel to look at yourself? To see yourself in your body, not just to check your outfit on your way out the door, but to spend some time here getting acquainted with your own, and your partner's, reflections.

Slowly, the partner behind can start to incorporate touch. If you're seated, perhaps begin in your partner's upper body at the neck and shoulders, collarbones, and chest, and work your way around here, down the length of the arms, up to the head, ears, face, and throat. Move slowly and intentionally around the body.

The partner receiving the touch is to let yourself fully receive the touch in each new place and watch through the mirror as touch interacts with the different parts of your body, stimulated further by the visual access that the mirror allows. Let yourself explore the use of the senses.

Sometimes it feels good to release control to our partners during this sort of receiving practice, to let them surprise you and guide the experience in a way that allows you to surrender fully into a more submissive role.

Other times, it feels good to verbally guide the touch you are receiving, perhaps by instructing your partner on where to touch you and what you want in each moment. Watch them as they touch you and see how it changes your relationship to being touched.

RECORD & REFLECT

Here is your space to reflect on this practice as a couple.
Take some time, be honest, and answer truthfully.

What was the main takeaway/lesson from this practice?

_____

_____

_____

_____

What did you like about this practice?

_____

_____

_____

_____

What was most challenging about this practice?

_____

_____

_____

_____

RATE THIS PRACTICE:

BORING/UNPLEASANT				FINE/HELPFUL			INSPIRING/SUPER FUN		
1	2	3	4	5	6	7	8	9	10

92
EYE/CONTACT

This one is borrowed from the tried and true, the traditional tantric practice of Eye Gazing, but incorporates some intentional physical contact to enhance connection.

THE PRACTICE

The practice of Eye Gazing is exactly as it sounds. It is the practice of intentionally gazing into your partner's eyes and having them gaze right back, for a prolonged period.

Often, this one starts out feeling quite uncomfortable since we are socially conditioned to feel extremely awkward when eye contact is held for more than a moment or two. However, what happens when we lean into this discomfort, as I mentioned in the previous exercise, has infinite potential.

This practice can be done in myriad positions; sitting, standing, laying down - whatever feels most comfy for you and your partner.

Close your eyes, take a breath or two, and when you're ready, open them back up together and, together, look directly into one another's eyes.

Let the first few moments be a time to sink in. Ride out the weirdness together, hold the gaze, and trust that after this initial hump of awkwardness the practice will get easier.

Here is where I'll invite the "contact" portion of the practice. Let your bodies gravitate toward one another.

Perhaps just your hands' touch; perhaps your legs intertwine. Make sure to keep enough distance between you so that the eye gazing is not broken or blurred. Too close contact can break the gaze, so stay at enough distance that you can fully maintain eye contact and focus here.

You can choose to set a timer for this practice if that feels more approachable, or you can choose to let it be more open-ended as we have discussed in the previous practices.

Let the timer be a gentle suggestion to move away from the gazing together and use the moments after its sounding to slowly exit the practice together.

If you'd rather not use a timer, then just let yourselves flow out of things together whenever and however it feels right.

RECORD & REFLECT

Here is your space to reflect on this practice as a couple.
Take some time, be honest, and answer truthfully.

What was the main takeaway/lesson from this practice?

_____

_____

_____

_____

What did you like about this practice?

_____

_____

_____

_____

What was most challenging about this practice?

_____

_____

_____

_____

RATE THIS PRACTICE:

BORING/UNPLEASANT				FINE/HELPFUL			INSPIRING/SUPER FUN		
1	2	3	4	5	6	7	8	9	10

93
PARTNERED YOGA

If you already have an established yoga practice, this one may be much easier for you. But still, you definitely enjoy partnered yoga even if you are both first-timers to the ancient practice.

THE PRACTICE

You can choose to seek out a proper partnered yoga class, or you can try to DIY the class experience, either by watching virtual partnered yoga classes online or by coming up with your own postures.

Essentially, you're engaging in yoga postures, both of you simultaneously, but the trick is to stay connected physically as you move from one posture to the next.

There are very specific methods to partnered yoga within the yogic philosophy, so if this is something you're more interested in doing some research is recommended.

However, if you're just interested in playing with the couple of positions you already know and want to see if you can do the whole thing while holding hands, then go for it!

The only rule is that you stay connected while trying to move from one posture to the next, in some way, so if you want to be formal about this practice, then you should seek traditional ways of moving in and out of partnered postures. Otherwise, maybe just decide on a way to stay connected and do the three postures you know from that month four years ago when you thought you'd become a yogi!

Play with putting your weight on your partner, trusting them to hold you from falling, and feel the energy flowing between your bodies as you practice together, in deep connection.

RECORD & REFLECT

Here is your space to reflect on this practice as a couple.
Take some time, be honest, and answer truthfully.

What was the main takeaway/lesson from this practice?

_____

_____

_____

_____

What did you like about this practice?

_____

_____

_____

_____

What was most challenging about this practice?

_____

_____

_____

_____

RATE THIS PRACTICE:

BORING/UNPLEASANT				FINE/HELPFUL			INSPIRING/SUPER FUN		
1	2	3	4	5	6	7	8	9	10

94
CONTACT IMPROV

This is similar to partnered yoga, but without all the structure and discipline that comes with the yogic philosophy. You can move however you want, so long as you stay connected to your partner's body in some way throughout the practice.

Contact improv is an improv practice that teaches its practitioners how to be in deep dialogue with their partners through embodiment, body language, and intuitive movement.

THE PRACTICE

Put on some music, dim the lights, and come together in the space. Listen to the music, and then at some point, one partner will decide to make contact with their partner.

The initiator guides the initial movement until both bodies sink into the movement, and from then on it will be a collaborative, improvised experience.

Essentially, the two of you are to move together, in contact with one another, completely improvising your movement, your flow, and how your bodies influence one another to move.

With this practice, you are encouraged to move freely and exploratively with your partner, to listen deeply to their body language and where and how it's guiding you with the music.

Try to go for at least one song but see how long it can last. How long can you creatively inspire one another's movements?

RECORD & REFLECT

Here is your space to reflect on this practice as a couple.
Take some time, be honest, and answer truthfully.

What was the main takeaway/lesson from this practice?

_____

_____

_____

_____

What did you like about this practice?

_____

_____

_____

_____

What was most challenging about this practice?

_____

_____

_____

_____

RATE THIS PRACTICE:

BORING/UNPLEASANT				FINE/HELPFUL			INSPIRING/SUPER FUN		
1	2	3	4	5	6	7	8	9	10

95

PLAYFIGHT/WRESTLING

This one is a fun way to get a little aggression out, while also rolling around with your partner and getting nice and close to their body without engaging in sex.

It can be very playful and silly but also quite kinky if you wish it to be. Many of us do love a good playfight, especially if we enjoy power play or role-play of the dom/sub nature.

THE PRACTICE

Find a relatively open space with enough room on the floor that you can roll around and not injure yourselves.

Agree on terms/boundaries (no shots to the face, don't go for the groin, etc.) and then commence wrestling. See if you can actually put some muscle into it if you're not usually a fighter. It can be a very safe way to get your emotions moving!

The first one to pin their partner down to the point of tapping out, wins. What do they win, you ask? Well, that's up to you to decide.

RECORD & REFLECT

Here is your space to reflect on this practice as a couple.
Take some time, be honest, and answer truthfully.

What was the main takeaway/lesson from this practice?

_____

_____

_____

_____

What did you like about this practice?

_____

_____

_____

_____

What was most challenging about this practice?

_____

_____

_____

_____

RATE THIS PRACTICE:

BORING/UNPLEASANT				FINE/HELPFUL			INSPIRING/SUPER FUN		
1	2	3	4	5	6	7	8	9	10

CHAPTER 12.

EXTRA NAUGHTY

INTRODUCTION TO EXTRA NAUGHTY

So, you've made it this far and you still want more, do you? By now you've ventured quite far into the world of sexual expansion and "spicing up your sex life," and you're still searching, still discovering yourself.

That desire to continue growing and exploring your sexual self is a beautiful thing, and if you've been able to get through to this part of this book, then you must already have gotten somewhat acquainted with your inner sexual self in a lot of different, perhaps new, ways.

These will only continue to re-affirm the validity of your needs and desires, not to mention, keep your relationship exciting and playful.

There is no going back once we begin to unleash the beast that is our inner sexual selves, both to ourselves and our partners, but I promise you, it's for the best both for yourself and for your relationship.

If we never started to peer into ourselves in this way, if that beast was never let out of the cage, somehow and in some way, that beast would escape when you least expect it, and that could cause a lot more damage than good.

All sexualities and sexual identities are safe if they're communicated about and respectful of the boundaries of all involved parties. Make sure you're on the same page as your partner, and then if you're both feeling confident in your experiences with all of these diverse and beautiful practices, it's time to travel even a little bit further, into the *Extra Naughty*.

96
PAIN PLAY/TORTURE PLAY

While we touched on pain and torture in the kink chapter, for those of us willing to push the envelope one step further, it is now time to explore the BDSM world of playing with pain. As we discussed during the *Spanko Practice*, leaning into pain can actually be a really powerful gateway to intensified pleasure. So, what happens if you intentionally torture your partner as a way of enhancing their pleasure?

THE PRACTICE

Try a form of stimulation that has not already been explored in your ventures through this book. There have been several different ways of engaging different senses suggested throughout the various sensory practices, and it's likely, you never tried them all each time.

Maybe you have yet to try using hot wax drips on your partner as a form of pain play, or maybe you haven't gone down the pin-wheel road yet. Maybe your partner would actually be open to letting you torture them in a sexy way (like holding a vibrator over the same spot on their clitoris even after they've had multiple orgasms). Maybe you could explore shock toys (toys that give little electric zaps to the skin when in contact with the body, like a dog's shock collar). Consider some of the types of pain that you'd both be interested in exploring, and then whatever you choose, as the receiver, it is your challenge to welcome the pain, to a tolerable degree, of course, and see how it can really enhance your experience.

FOR EXAMPLE:

If you're being shocked across the breasts but then fingered at the same time, can you focus on the pleasure happening in your genitals, and let the pain of the shock cause you to feel the pleasure even more?

258

RECORD & REFLECT

Here is your space to reflect on this practice as a couple.
Take some time, be honest, and answer truthfully.

What was the main takeaway/lesson from this practice?

_____

_____

_____

_____

What did you like about this practice?

_____

_____

_____

_____

What was most challenging about this practice?

_____

_____

_____

_____

RATE THIS PRACTICE:

BORING/UNPLEASANT				FINE/HELPFUL			INSPIRING/SUPER FUN		
1	2	3	4	5	6	7	8	9	10

97

TICKLE TORTURE

Tickle torture can arguably be much harder to endure than pain play, which is why it's, well, torture. In medieval times, tickle torture was used as one of the many gruesome forms of torture to the death (that's right, it can literally cause death!), and is widely regarded as one of the worst forms of torture.

With all that said, please proceed safely and be very clear about safe words and boundaries, but know that like all other kinks, tickle torture can be enjoyed as a pleasure-enhancing practice.

THE PRACTICE

Choose who will adopt the dom and sub roles.

Most commonly, folks go for the feet with this one. The feet are generally the most ticklish part of the body due to the many, many nerve endings on the soles of the feet, but this will depend on each individual's body and sensitive areas.

Either using bondage or another form of restraint to your liking, the dom will place the sub in a position where the body part they want to focus on for tickling is accessible to the dom, but the sub will not be able to pull away from the sensations as they grow increasingly intense. This is torture, after all.

Use some form of tickling device, perhaps a feather or a wire brush, and start slowly on the body part(s) you've decided to focus on to begin.

While your sub may be laughing, remember that they are most likely not laughing because anything is funny. Laughter is often aroused by the nerves being stimulated by the tickling. In this regard, make sure to stay aware of the changes in your sub's behavior.

Using different ticking methods, travel around your sub's body a little bit and stimulate them with tickling wherever you think they may be ticklish. Some common places are the back and sides of the neck, the armpits, the ribcage, the back, the buttocks, the back of the knees, and the inner elbows.

There are many options; it just depends on what you know about your sub and their body pleasure.

Once you feel you've given them enough torture, you can decide to pleasure them however you wish, to bring them back down into their body by caressing them in a nice and slow, very grounding way.

Try not to go straight for the genitals, but rather place your hands facing down on their torso, their chest, over their eyes, and so on. Just as a way of literally grounding them down in your own hands to help their breathing and mind return to normal. It will be nice for them, having just been so tense and overstimulated via the tickling, to have some firm, heavy hands on their body.

RECORD & REFLECT

Here is your space to reflect on this practice as a couple.
Take some time, be honest, and answer truthfully.

What was the main takeaway/lesson from this practice?

_____

_____

_____

_____

What did you like about this practice?

_____

_____

_____

_____

What was most challenging about this practice?

_____

_____

_____

_____

RATE THIS PRACTICE:

BORING/UNPLEASANT				FINE/HELPFUL			INSPIRING/SUPER FUN		
1	2	3	4	5	6	7	8	9	10

98

"MY PET"

Going back to kink and BDSM once again, this one takes it a couple of steps further from merely assigning roles of dom and sub within your dynamic. This time you really are going to take power play into a more elongated state of play, a more degradation-based experience.

THE PRACTICE

First, choose who is acting as the dom and sub.

Dom, your sub is your pet and therefore is cared for and allowed freedom, food, activity, and affection at your mercy. Because of this, it is key to decide on a time frame and parameters prior to entering into this practice.

The sub will be kept in a space from which they cannot escape (maybe a basement, handcuffed or leashed to a certain space, or if you've fully committed to the pet thing, in a large enough cage to trap a human with). Now you're ready to see how it feels to regard your lover as your pet. You can go for walks and go about your daily life, knowing full well there's a human in a cage if your care, waiting for you to play with them.

The sub is the pet; therefore, the sub willingly crawls into the confined space their dom has ordered them into, and simply, the sub has to wait for their dom to get home and let them out to play. This is a very real iteration of the master/slave practices, as the master can leave their sub/slave locked in their room or confinement space for as long as they want, within reason, while the sub merely waits, in anticipation, for what their master has in store for them. When the dom finally comes back, they ask their sub if they were a good boy/girl and if they deserve to come out of the cage. After going back and forth and engaging in dom/sub roles/energies verbally, the dom will bring their pet out to play.

RECORD & REFLECT

Here is your space to reflect on this practice as a couple.
Take some time, be honest, and answer truthfully.

What was the main takeaway/lesson from this practice?

_____

_____

_____

_____

What did you like about this practice?

_____

_____

_____

_____

What was most challenging about this practice?

_____

_____

_____

_____

RATE THIS PRACTICE:

BORING/UNPLEASANT				FINE/HELPFUL			INSPIRING/SUPER FUN		
1	2	3	4	5	6	7	8	9	10

99

THE MORE
THE MERRIER

Have you and your partner had the threesome conversation yet? Have you dabbled in the world of polyamory? If this is something you've explored within your partnership thus far, then perhaps it's time to re-visit and experiment further with the wonderful world of a "the more the merrier" mentality.

But if this is something that has felt shaky or intimidating up until now, have no fear - there are many ways to explore polyamory and additional partners within your already established relationship that can be exciting and enriching for both partners involved. So, let's dig in.

THE PRACTICE

Often folks ask when discussing the desire to have a threesome, "But where will we find someone?"

One of the most common ways to find a third person to join sexy time in our online world is, well you guessed it, dating apps. Many people find it fun to make a profile on widely used dating apps such as Tinder or Hinge as a couple and write in their bio that they're seeking a third person specifically to add another member to their sexual relationship.

It is also possible to find interested thirds the old-fashioned way, through meeting new people at bars and out in social settings.

If you're interested in joining a local community of sexually explorative folks, looking into joining kink communities in your locale can also be a really good way to explore new connections together.

If three is a number you're more than familiar with, maybe it's time to explore sex with another couple, making four of you collectively having sex with one another. There are really no limits to how many parties can get involved; it's all about your desires and comfortability.

The initiating of *The More The Merrier* can be the tricky part, so do your best to release any fear of doing or saying the wrong thing, and really just lean into the sexual energy you feel in the room.

If you feel called to initiate, start with all three (or more) of you on a bed or in a close space, and gently start caressing one of your partner's thighs while starting to kiss another partner. Keep everyone involved, especially the third person that doesn't already have an established sexual relationship with your partner and yourself.

Try not to just focus on your partner but continue to validate them so there are no jealous feelings needed.

Go about foreplay and engaging in sex as you normally would, and if you're not currently the one being pleasured, then find a way to assist in pleasuring one, or both, of your partners. Get creative with how to continue to involve one another.

If you're with more than one other person, see if you can continuously switch things up. Who is pleasuring who? Who are you focusing on? Can you try to pleasure more than one person at once? Can you receive from more than one person at once?

Push your notions of sex past the idea of monogamy. It can be very expansive - and very sexy!

RECORD & REFLECT

Here is your space to reflect on this practice as a couple.
Take some time, be honest, and answer truthfully.

What was the main takeaway/lesson from this practice?

_____

_____

_____

_____

What did you like about this practice?

_____

_____

_____

_____

What was most challenging about this practice?

_____

_____

_____

_____

RATE THIS PRACTICE:

BORING/UNPLEASANT				FINE/HELPFUL			INSPIRING/SUPER FUN		
1	2	3	4	5	6	7	8	9	10

100

BUILDING
A RED ROOM

If you've ever watched any BDSM pornography or media, or read *50 Shades of Grey*, then you're familiar with the concept of a Red Room. Simply, a Red Room is a designated room in your house (or outside of your house) that is exclusively designed and used for sex.

Often, kinky folk find the use of a Red Room very helpful in setting their BDSM dynamic apart from their daily lives, so that once the two of you enter the Red Room, kink and the dynamics/behavior that comes with it commences, and once you leave the Red Room, those roles stay behind. It can act as a way of giving consent to begin BDSM play, as to enter the room is to enter the subspace, and it is a safe space for play.

It is also helpful logistically if you have a plethora of toys and apparatuses for play that you need to store or leave set up - it can just be a much easier way of accessing all of the fun things you wish to play with. But, realistically, we don't all have an extra room in our house to designate specifically for our kink lives, so how can we create a sex room within our means?

THE PRACTICE

If you have a spare room in your house, a storage room, a guest room, or even a space in your basement, then this practice will be much easier for you than for the folks that live in small apartments in the city and have trouble even finding space for all their clothing.

However, there is always a way to get around space limitations if you're determined to create your sexy fantasy, so the first step is to start looking around the space you have access to in a new way. Where could you carve out a little space for designated playtime?

Once you've decided on a space (a whole room, or even just a corner or a walk-in closet) you can start to design together. Think about the senses. What colors arouse you? What textures feel sexy against your skin? What is the lighting situation like in your dream sexy space? Do you have candles and rose petals, or is it all latex and leather?

You can refer back to the questions we went through when exploring our *Alter Egos* in the Role-Play chapter. These types of questions can be very useful in getting to know your sexual selves and designing space for them.

Once you have some mood ideas (colors, textures, lighting, etc.), you can start to think logistically. Would you like to have a whole bed in your Red Room, or is a massage table, or even just a chair or couch adequate for what the two of you like to get into? Do you need rigging to hang from the ceiling, hooks for bondage to connect to, or a system for playing music?

How can you make this space conducive to your particular kinks and fantasies together?

Have fun creating this space together!

Once it's finished, see if you can keep it just for yourselves. Make it a sacred space for just the two of you to play -- unless you have additional partners, of course. See how it feels to use it in different ways, as a portal into your kink personas, or as a place to turn to for inspiration.

Use it and design it however you wish. This is your opportunity to give your sexual selves everything they desire!

RECORD & REFLECT

Here is your space to reflect on this practice as a couple.
Take some time, be honest, and answer truthfully.

What was the main takeaway/lesson from this practice?

_____

_____

_____

_____

What did you like about this practice?

_____

_____

_____

_____

What was most challenging about this practice?

_____

_____

_____

_____

RATE THIS PRACTICE:

BORING/UNPLEASANT				FINE/HELPFUL			INSPIRING/SUPER FUN		
1	2	3	4	5	6	7	8	9	10

101
HOW TO THROW A SEX PARTY

So, you've made it all the way through. Pat yourself on the back! It's not easy to push your comfort zone so far beyond the mainstream in a sexual way, but you've swum with the currents and ended up here, with a wealth of knowledge about yourself and your partner, and hopefully, plenty of orgasms and sexy memories to hold onto as you continue to unravel your sexual selves together - plus keep things spicy moving forward into the rest of your sex life.

Now, we can celebrate - let's throw a party!

THE PRACTICE

Throwing a sex party may sound crazy, and ultimately it can be, but crazy isn't always bad. It can be really fun!

It's just like any other party, but you may just want to consider things in a little more detail when planning. You'll most likely want to choose a theme and a way of bringing folks in that can be engaging and remove tension/awkwardness. First and foremost, however, you'll want to curate a guest list with only individuals that you know are safe and sex-positive.

Also, you'll need to find yourself in a safe location that you know will not put anyone in jeopardy. For this reason, it is often best to plan a sex party to be held at your own home, with a circle of guests that you know intimately.

When your guests arrive, it is common to engage everyone in some cocktails and some ice-breaker games/activities. Think of some ideas that make you feel comfortable when you enter a new crowd.

Go around the room and have everyone share the name they'd like to be called in that space, whether they are a dom or sub, what they enjoy and are open to, and what boundaries they may have (things they do not want to do, their "no's").

Block off any visibility from the outside, so this remains a safe space.

To begin pairing up or initiating sexy time, you can play games that we've discussed throughout this book such as *Jar of Desire, Sexy Twister, Sexy Decks, Kinky Dice,* or any of the other practices we've explored together that feel conducive to a group setting. You're all here for the same reason, so have fun exploring with like-minded people!

RECORD & REFLECT

Here is your space to reflect on this practice as a couple.
Take some time, be honest, and answer truthfully.

What was the main takeaway/lesson from this practice?

_____

_____

_____

_____

What did you like about this practice?

_____

_____

_____

_____

What was most challenging about this practice?

_____

_____

_____

_____

RATE THIS PRACTICE:

BORING/UNPLEASANT				FINE/HELPFUL			INSPIRING/SUPER FUN		
1	2	3	4	5	6	7	8	9	10

CONCLUSION

While the practices and games in this book are diverse and expand across several boundaries and genres of sexuality and gender, know that the fun does not stop here. The beautiful thing about humans is that we are constantly evolving and changing, so in reality, if you put the time and energy in, you will be able to continue to explore one another's desires, kinks, and spicey new curiosities in the bedroom for the rest of your lives if you choose to. It is all a choice, and the choice is yours each time you engage in intimacy with one another.

Sticking to the old routine is nice here and there, but the main reason couples fall into a sexual rut at some point along their journey is simply that they get lazy, lose inspiration, and forget how dynamic and intriguing their partner is.

To avoid this dulling of the sexual vibrancy that is your relationship at its finest, I encourage you to take the time to reflect on your journey here, either in the spaces provided or in your own minds, or with each other. What were the practices or sections that stuck out to you? What were the things you want to go back to or do differently? What did you hate?

Use this reflection as a way of laying out the next adventures to take as you close this book and move forward in your sexual journeys. Whatever you found interesting or aroused by, revisit it, change it, manipulate it, make it your own, push your limits and the limits of this book, and see what's really out there for you.

This book is merely a guide in 101 directions you could take your sexual relationship, but there are infinite possibilities! Stay connected, and I'll say it again, communicate, as you explore, but also encourage one another to continue to challenge and inspire one another, and continue to play!

You are sexually powerful humans, so don't ever stop exploring your power!

Made in the USA
Las Vegas, NV
29 December 2022

64376484R10155